GET
Ready!

A STEP-BY-STEP PLANNER

for MAINTAINING YOUR

FINANCIAL FIRST AID KIT

TONY STEUER, CLU, LA, CPFFE

LIFE
INSURANCE
SAGE
PRESS

Published by Life Insurance Sage Press
Alameda, CA
tonysteuer.com

Distributed by River Grove Books

Design and composition by Greenleaf Book Group
Cover design by Greenleaf Book Group
Icons from www.flaticon.com. Inclined Pencil made by Nice and Serious; Printer made by monkik; Medical History made by Linector; First Aid Kit, Stethoscope, and Heartbeat made by Freepik

Publisher's Cataloging-in-Publication data is available.

Print ISBN: 978-0-692-16392-4
eBook ISBN-13: 978-1-7342100-0-2

First Edition

To my wife, Cheryl, who is my beloved partner
and always supports my writing and advocacy work.

To my son, Avery, who is my hero
as he meets the challenge of living life with Type 1 diabetes.

To my friend and colleague Neil Granger, who always listens and provides wise counsel.

To all the readers of my books and articles, thank you for your support.

Live life expecting the worst, hoping for the best, and living for the future!
—Jerry Garcia

Contents

Introduction   1

    🧰 GET READY!

Chapter 1: How to Use This Planner   5

    📋 The Check-In Gauge

    Creating a GET READY! Binder for Documents

    Sign Up for the GET READY! Email Newsletter

    Stepping In

Chapter 2: Creating Your Financial First Aid Kit   9

    Emergency Contacts

    Personal Papers and Legal Documents

    Critical Emergency Action List

    Contents of Wallet

    Storing Documents and Valuables

        Storage Unit

    Personal Information

    Children

        Grandchildren

    Health (Medical) Information

    Pet Information

    Military Service

    Memberships: Clubs and Organizations

        Charitable Organizations

    Digital Life (Devices and Services)

        Tracking Your Log-In Credentials

    Reward and Loyalty Programs

Chapter 3: Listing Your Assets   39

    Checking and Savings Accounts

    Certificates of Deposit (CDs)

    Stocks

    Bonds

        Treasury Securities (Bills and Bonds)

        Corporate Bonds, Government Agency Bonds, and Municipal Bonds

    Mutual Funds

    Exchange-Traded Funds (ETFs)

    Collectibles

Stock Options

Business Interests/Ownerships

Royalties (Copyrights, Trademarks, Patents, and Other Property That Can Be Licensed)

Debts and Obligations Owed to You (Loans You Have Made)

College Savings Accounts

ABLE Accounts

Chapter 4: Organizing Your Retirement Plan   **65**

Individual Retirement Accounts (IRAs)

Self-Employed and Small Business Individual Retirement Accounts

Employer Retirement Accounts

    401(k), 403(b), and 457 Plans

    Pension Plans

Other Employer and Group Retirement Plans

Social Security

Chapter 5: Listing Your Home and Real Estate/Real Property   **79**

Home (Primary Residence)

Vacation Home/Secondary Residence

Time-Share/Vacation Club

Investment Property

Farmland

Undeveloped Land

Commercial Property

Cars

Planes, Boats, and Recreational Vehicles

Taking Inventory of Major Property

Chapter 6: Compiling Your Income (Earnings)   **95**

Create Your Total Compensation Statement

    Cash Compensation

    Paid Time Off

    Group (Employee) Benefits and Deductions

    Total Compensation

    Dependents Coverage

Other Earned Income: Second Job, Sharing (Gig) Economy, Side-Hustle

Online Income/Sales

Royalties (Copyrights, Trademarks, Patents, and Other Property That Can Be Licensed)

Investment Income

Retirement Income

Chapter 7: Organizing Your Debts, Personal Loans, Living Expenses, and Taxes   **109**

    Car Loans and Leases

    Home Loan (Mortgage)

        Home Equity Loans (Second Mortgages)

        Private Mortgage Insurance

        Vacation Home (Second Home) Loans

        Time-Share and Vacation Club Loans

        Reverse Mortgage

    Student Loans

    Investment Property Loans

    Business (Commercial) Property Loan

    Personal Debts and Loans

    Credit Cards

    Debt Consolidation Loans

    Living Expenses

        Renting and Leasing a Residence

        Utility and Household Bills

    Education, Care, and Support: Child Care, Day Care, Tuition, and Adult Care

    Subscriptions and Services

    Memberships, Season Tickets, Clubs, and Organizations

    Taxes

        Tax Documents

        Property Taxes

Chapter 8: Assembling Your Insurance Portfolio   **141**

    Auto Insurance

    Disability Insurance

    Health Insurance and Health Care Costs

        Short-Term Health Insurance Plans

        Dental Insurance

        Vision Insurance

        Medicare

    Homeowners and Renters Insurance

    Life Insurance

    Long-Term Care Insurance

    Annuities

    Miscellaneous Insurance Policies

Chapter 9: Estate Planning   **171**

    Power of Attorney

    Health Care Directives/Advanced Directive/Health Care Power of Attorney

Final Arrangements

    Letter of Intent/Letter of Instruction

    Donation of Organs or Body

Burial and Cremation

    Viewings, Visitations, and Wakes

    Funeral and Memorial Services

    Celebration of Life Ceremony and Reception

    Obituary

Ethical Will

Wills

Trusts

Digital Estate Planning

Pet Estate Planning

Chapter 10: Evaluating Your Financial Readiness   **191**

Creating a Cash Flow Analysis and Budget

Knowing Your Net Worth

Retirement Planning Tracker

    Your Retirement Timeline

    How Much Will You Need to Have Saved for Retirement

Financial Ratios

Chapter 11: Staying Ready   **215**

Financial Calendar

Financial One-Time Events

Protecting Your Information: Credit Report Monitoring

Navigating Your Credit Report

Identity Theft

Credit Scores

Specialty Consumer Reporting Companies

Final Words   **227**

Appendix: Stepping In   **229**

A Note from the Author   **233**

Index   **235**

About the Author   **245**

Introduction

By failing to prepare, you are preparing to fail.
—Benjamin Franklin

For a guy who's been in the insurance and financial business for the past 30-plus years, you'd think I would know how to handle the affairs upon the death of a loved one. But there I was, shortly after my mother died, searching for where I should start. I didn't know where her bank statements were; I couldn't find her car title; I had no idea how many bills she owed or whether she still had a safe-deposit box.

I wasn't prepared.

This is especially odd for me, because not only am I well versed in insurance and personal finance, I've also been an avid outdoor-adventurer, along with having a son with Type 1 diabetes. Any time I prepare my family for a trip, I always begin by packing a first aid kit that includes all of the items necessary to manage his diabetes. I assemble the insulin, pump supplies, testing kit supplies, and much more, along with typical first aid supplies such as bandages, ointments, and moleskin. I know the importance of being prepared.

So when I was called on to be the executor for my mother's estate, I found myself lacking in two areas—financial know-how and disaster preparedness—that I am generally on top of.

All of this got me thinking about how I could help others avoid the kind of situation I found myself in, and even how I could have helped my mother before she passed. That's when the idea of creating a "GET READY!" binder took shape. In the months after tidying up her estate, I refined my ideas on the book you're holding in your hands.

GET READY! A Step-by-Step Planner for Maintaining Your Financial First Aid Kit is the kind of book I wish I'd had before I was called upon to take care of my mother's affairs. It's designed to help you no matter what your age or circumstance—whether

GET READY! STANDS FOR:

- **G**oals: It's important to have financial goals so that you can be in charge of your financial future. Taking time to make a plan now will allow you to be prepared, rather than having to scramble to gather information when it's needed.

- **E**ducate Yourself: Become financially literate. Take the time to understand your financial life. Money is an important part of life, so it's worth your time to understand all the different components of your financial life. Most people spend more time researching a new television than making financial decisions, so do your research on all aspects of your financial life. Never make a financial decision that you don't understand. Instead, keep it simple.

- **T**rack: It's important to keep an eye on all areas of your financial life in order to stay on the path to achieving your goals.

Continued on next page . . .

- **R**eview for Accuracy and Fit: After determining that a financial product will fit your goals, determine which product configuration is right for you. Make sure to evaluate all of your options. If you need help, seek a qualified advisor.
- **E**xpenses: Do you know what you're paying for? Watch your expenses/costs. It's common to think only about the primary cost of an asset or an investment along with the expected return. However, there are often hidden costs and high expenses that increase the amount of money you pay for something, and this can eat into the return on your investment. You may not be able to make significant adjustments to your income; however, you can make adjustments to your costs.
- **A**ssemble Information: Most of us have our financial life scattered in many places. Take the time to bring it all together by documenting it in this planner and adding it to your GET READY! binder (see Chapter 1).
- **D**etails: Take the time to review the details of financial products and services. As John Wooden said, "It's the little details that are vital. Little things make big things happen." Make smart and realistic financial decisions. A good rule of thumb is, if it sounds too good to be true, then it probably is. And remember that the details include protecting your financial life by having appropriate insurance.
- **Y**early Review: Life is full of changes. It's important to monitor all aspects of your financial life to see if changes should be made and if you are maximizing value. The financial calendar on page "Financial Calendar" on page 216 will help you stay on track. Part of this includes doing a financial background check (credit reports and so on) to make sure your financial history is correct.

you are new parents starting out in your careers, or mid-stride with growing bank accounts, or thinking about retiring any day now. Everyone needs to keep track of their finances, and—as I learned the hard way—the best way to keep these records is updated and in one place (with a backup, of course).

While this kit includes a lot of information, including some that may not apply to your situation, it's also designed to point you in the right direction to help you make important changes, and to urge you to ask questions and become better educated about your finances.

This book is designed to be a financial companion. Whether you need to organize your finances in the event of a disaster (emergency evacuation) or when applying for a loan or reviewing assets for retirement, this book will make your life easier. It will also help you prepare for death or a situation in which someone has to step in to manage your financial life. Finally, it will help you maximize your existing resources by spotting any gaps in your financial plan while eliminating any unnecessary or duplicative financial products and services.

BENEFITS OF HAVING A FINANCIAL FIRST AID KIT

When you put together an emergency kit or a first aid kit, your hope is that you never have to use it. Or that if you do, it's only for something minor, like needing a Band-Aid. However, since life is uncertain, and things happen, your emergency kit needs to be stocked with tools to address all types of situations. If you don't have the right tools, you may not be able to deal with a specific situation.

It's important to complete this planner and keep it in a safe place; you might even need to take it with you in the event of an emergency. This planner will also ensure that your family will be able to locate and manage your financial affairs, allowing them access to all of your assets and accounts in the event of your death or incapacity. Making a copy of this information and keeping it in a safe place is important so that the information is not lost in a fire or flood or simply misplaced.

Completing this planner will also put you in charge of all aspects of your financial life, which makes it a lifesaver in the event of any kind of disaster. You can use this planner to organize and communicate important information. By doing so, you will both gain peace of mind and ensure that you are maximizing all areas of your financial life.

This planner will provide guidance on creating a GET READY! binder for your important documents. Completing the GET READY! binder will allow you to easily compile and access the underlying documentation for information in this planner. Your GET READY! binder should also be stored in a secure location that you can quickly access.

All forms included in this book are also available on my website for download at www.tonysteuer.com /resources, so that you can fill them out electronically and include them in your GET READY! binders.

 GET READY!

Before taking any action, you have to prepare. Proper preparation requires having the right mindset along with an adaptive system to help you achieve your goals. Back when I was a first responder for wilderness outings, I always made sure to assemble a first aid kit, which included supplies to cover possible injuries and even rescues. For example, if there were going to be any long-distance hikes, I packed extra bandages and cream to treat blisters.

Just like first responders who need to prepare for emergencies, we all have unique needs and financial lives that require careful planning and preparation. The phrase "GET READY!" can be applied to all facets of your financial life and is designed to help you have a checklist for all situations. First responders use a SOAP report as a common way to evaluate and manage injuries. A SOAP report is a form of documentation that includes four areas: subjective, objective, assessment, and plan. Subjective is what the issue is, also known as the chief complaint. Objective refers to the facts, such as vital signs. Assessment is the diagnosis. And Plan lays out how to proceed.

In this book, the "GET READY!" system is your financial equivalent of a SOAP report. You will see this heading appear at the beginning of each chapter to help you compile all of the necessary elements to be as prepared as you can be in each major financial area of your life.

Take a moment to do an assessment of your financial preparedness before you get started by taking the Financial Preparedness Quiz at www.tonysteuer.com. You'll receive a Financial Preparedness Score with a customized to-do list and monthly email reminders to keep you on track as you complete and maintain your planner.

CHAPTER 1

How to Use This Planner

The best first aid kit is the one that you have with you.

A first aid kit won't help you if you don't know how to use the various components. Learning how to use the various components requires education and training. Just like your first aid kit, the more that you put into this planner, the more you'll get out of it.

The planner is designed to walk you through your financial life to help you gather and document all of your information in one place. Think of it as having a full financial check-up. When a first responder does an assessment of a patient, they do a complete head-to-toe exam that is supplemented by more detailed assessments when a specific issue is spotted. Similar to a first responder's comprehensive exam, this planner will guide you through a full exam of your financial life while allowing you to add in details for the specific sections that apply to you.

The "GET READY!" system that we discussed in the Introduction will guide you through each chapter. The planner is designed for you to fill out at your own pace, step-by-step, rather than in one marathon cram session.

 THE CHECK-IN GAUGE

This planner uses a check-in gauge to help you track your progress through each chapter and to provide guidance through an overall tracker. The check-in appears at the end of each chapter and enables you to see if an area is not applicable, in process, or completed.

To supplement this planner, I recommend that you put together a companion GET READY! binder along with a flash drive or cloud account to back up your documents. For sensitive documents, such as passports, Social Security cards, and marriage and birth certificates, you will want a fireproof safe or safe-deposit box.

Your GET READY! binder will have the paper copies of your major financial documents that are not stored in a secure location. In each section, there is information about what you should consider adding to the GET READY! binder. Paperwork that you'll want to put in your GET READY! binder includes such items as insurance policies and certificates, bank account details, investment statements, loan documents, and estate planning documents.

As you work through the planner, you'll be guided on what to add to your GET READY! binder, as well as what to put in your safe or to back up with your USB thumb drive or cloud account. This is just like putting together a first aid kit, where items are added as you go through a checklist of basic needs and possible emergencies.

CREATING A GET READY! BINDER FOR DOCUMENTS

Here's a list of what you will need for your GET READY! binder, at least to start with:

- Three-ring GET READY! binder (I recommend the Case-it Mighty Zip Tab 3-Inch Zipper binder, Red, D-146-RED, available from Amazon.com.)
- Dividers, with tabs to write on. (As you work through the planner, you may decide to split some of these sections up or add different ones.) I suggest starting with the following tabs:
  - Creating Your Financial First Aid Kit
  - Assets
  - Retirement Plans
  - Home and Real Property
  - Income
  - Debts, Loans, Expenses, and Taxes
  - Insurance
  - Estate Planning
  - Financial Calendar & Credit Reports
- Transparent document holders (at least 25)

Other items* you should consider include whichever of the following options that work best for you:

- Fire-proof safe to store important documents that need to be secure
- Safe-deposit box to store important documents
- Cloud storage account, such as Apple iCloud or Dropbox, to back up all digital financial documents
- USB (thumb) drive to store digital documents that can be kept in your safe or GET READY! binder

*I recommend these backup options for your binder because it's always good to have multiple backups in case one gets lost.

SIGN UP FOR THE GET READY! EMAIL NEWSLETTER

The GET READY! newsletter will provide regular tips designed to help you stay on track to complete the planner and to maintain it. It will also keep you up to date on the latest in financial preparedness. You can sign up at www.tonysteuer.com/newsletter.

STEPPING IN

At the end of the planner you'll find an Appendix item called Stepping In. This is to be used by those who have to take the helm of your financial ship in the event of your death or incapacity. Be sure to let your loved ones know where your planner and binder are so that when it is time to "step in," they will be well informed and able to take action right away.

CHAPTER 2

Creating Your Financial First Aid Kit

It wasn't raining when Noah built the ark.
—Howard Ruff

Having a financial emergency plan in the form of a financial first aid kit will benefit you in several ways. First, it will allow you to maintain quick access to your financial life. Second, it will enable you to easily gather information in the event of a disaster. And third, it will enable you to leave behind a financial first aid kit for your heirs. The kit will provide them with the information they need to quickly learn about and be able to take control of your financial commitments at the time of your passing. Whether you have limited funds or significant assets, your financial life will need to be wrapped up in the event something happens to you. Preparing now is easier than making others sort through files and piles of paper later.

The Federal Emergency Management Agency's website notes that evacuations are a fairly common occurrence in the United States. Aside from natural disasters such as fires, earthquakes, and hurricanes, people are often told to leave their homes due to transportation and industrial accidents.

Planning for an emergency is a critical step to financial success. We make plans and then life happens. It's important for us to take the time while we have the time to make a plan. Organization is the key to a successful financial plan. If you were given five minutes to gather all of your important belongings, what would you do?

WHAT TO INCLUDE IN YOUR FINANCIAL FIRST AID KIT

Most of us think about emergency planning and have a first aid kit or some basic supplies. A "financial first aid kit," however, is usually not part of the usual emergency planning process. But it should be. And your financial first aid kit needs to be in an easily accessible and easy-to-remember location so that it can be quickly collected in the event of an emergency. In fact, your kit may not make it through an emergency, so be sure to have a back-up kit on a cloud account, on a thumb drive, or in a safe-deposit box.

 **GET READY!**

In this chapter, we will share how you can become more financially ready. You will learn about—

1. **Emergency contacts.** You will be making a list of all your important contacts, including family, friends, neighbors, medical providers, and advisors.

2. **Personal papers and legal documents.** You'll also want to compile your important documents and identification, including medical information (e.g., immunization records), passports (originals or copies), drivers' licenses, birth and marriage certificates, adoption decrees, Social Security cards, military records, insurance policies, and paperwork for pets. This vital information will enable you to access your financial accounts and property, obtain disaster relief, file insurance claims, and receive appropriate medical services.

3. **Critical emergency action list.** You'll create a list of critical steps to take in the event of an emergency, including an evacuation.

4. **Contents of wallet.** You will list everything you carry in your wallet in the event that it is lost or stolen.

5. **Storing documents and valuables.** You'll create an inventory of items kept in your personal safe, safe-deposit box, and storage unit.

6. **Personal information.** In this section, you'll add all of your background information.

7. **Children and grandchildren.** You'll add important information about your children and grandchildren.

8. **Health (medical) information.** Here's where you can keep track of your medical history, treatments, and medications.

9. **Pet information.** You'll add details regarding these members of your household: dates of birth, dates and proof of vaccination, names of vets, and so on.

10. **Military service.** Include years and branch of the service you served, pertinent details about discharge (if necessary), and decorations.

11. **Memberships: clubs and organizations.** Include clubs and organizations, both personal and professional, to which you belong. You can also note your place of worship and charitable organizations you support.

12. **Digital life (devices and services).** Write down log-in information needed to access your digital devices and services, such as your email and social media accounts.

13. **Reward and loyalty programs.** Here is where you can enter information about frequent flyer miles and hotel rewards programs.

Emergency Contacts

Knowing who to call in an emergency is important for you, your spouse, and your heirs. These names and numbers will be a useful resource for others who need to manage your financial ship. **Table 1** will help you list all of your contacts in one easy-to-access location.

Table 1: Emergency Contacts

Emergency Contacts	Name	Phone Number	Email Address
Emergency contact 1			
Emergency contact 2			
Emergency contact 3			
Closest living relative			
Executor			
Trustee			
Attorney			
Banker			
Accountant			
Financial planner			
Business partner			
Employer			
Physician(s): primary, specialty, dentist (include names for spouse & child)			
Pharmacy			
Home health agency			
Veterinarian			
Neighbor(s)			
Babysitter			
School (and day care)			
Auto repair			
Electrician			
Plumber			
Appliance repair person			
Heating/air conditioning			
Other			

Continued on next page . . . ➡

NEXT STEP

Keep a copy of this list with your secure documents and add a copy to the Creating Your Financial First Aid Kit section of your GET READY! binder.

Personal Papers and Legal Documents

Being able to quickly find your important documents will help your spouse, children, or executor in the event you become incapacitated or pass away. It will also help you during your life—when you apply for a loan, meet with your estate planning attorney, or are forced to leave your house in an emergency. You can accomplish this by fully completing this planner and assembling your GET READY! binder. Keep in mind that this is *your* planner, and you can complete as much or as little as you want. The more you complete, however, the more useful it becomes.

In **Table 2**, you'll enter the physical location of your most important documents. As you complete this planner, you'll walk through the details of these documents and where they fit into your financial life. Be sure to take your time and complete this as accurately as you can.

Table 2: Personal Papers and Legal Documents

Document	Location	How Long to Keep
Address book (personal)		N/A
Address book (business)		N/A
Birth certificate		Forever
Charitable membership & volunteer documents		As needed
Children(s) legal documents (such as birth certificate & Social Security card)		Forever
Citizenship documents		Forever
Club documents		Forever
Divorce decrees		Forever
Educational transcripts		Forever
Loyalty program information		As long as participating
Marriage license		Forever
Medical records		Forever
Military records & documents		Forever
Naturalization documents		Forever

Document	Location	How Long to Keep
Passport		Until update
Password list		Forever
Pet documents		As long as you have pet
Religious documents		N/A
Reward program information		As long as participating
Safe-deposit box agreement		Until agreement is canceled
Service club documents		N/A
Storage unit agreements		Until agreement is canceled
Other personal documents		Varies

ASSETS

Document	Location	How Long to Keep
Bank account records		Keep statements & canceled checks for 6 years (receipts until statement reconciliation)
Brokerage account records		Keep purchase records or transaction confirmations and annual statements for 6 years after tax deadline for year of sale.
Business interests documents		Forever
Certificate of deposit records		Keep purchase records or transaction confirmations and annual statements for 6 years after tax deadline for year of sale.
Collectibles inventory		Keep purchase records or transaction confirmations and annual statements for 6 years after tax deadline for year of sale.
College savings accounts documents		Keep purchase records or transaction confirmations and annual statements for 6 years after tax deadline for year of sale.
Debts (owed to you) records		Until updated or paid off (though keep indefinitely as proof of payoff)
Financial planning documents		Until updated
Investment records		Keep purchase records or transaction confirmations and annual statements for 6 years after tax deadline for year of sale.
Royalty agreements and records		Forever
Other assets		Varies

Continued on next page . . .

Document	Location	How Long to Keep

RETIREMENT PLANS

Document	Location	How Long to Keep
Individual retirement account records (IRA, SEP)		Keep purchase records or transaction confirmations and annual statements for 6 years after tax deadline for year of account closure.
Employer retirement account records (401(k), 403(b), 457)		Keep purchase records or transaction confirmations and annual statements for 6 years after tax deadline for year of account closure.
Pension plan information		Keep purchase records or transaction confirmations and annual statements for 6 years after tax deadline for year of account closure.
Social Security card & statements		Keep purchase records or transaction confirmations and annual statements for 6 years after tax deadline for year of account closure.
Other retirement plan information & documents		Keep purchase records or transaction confirmations and annual statements for 6 years after tax deadline for year of account closure.

HOME AND REAL ESTATE (REAL PROPERTY)

Document	Location	How Long to Keep
Appliance receipts and warranty information		Until sold or discarded
Car (title, registration, repair records)		Until 6 months after sale
Commercial property records		Keep on hand for at least 6 years after sale of property.
Electronics (computers & entertainment) receipts and warranty information		Until sold or discarded
Farmland records		Keep on hand for at least 6 years after sale of property.
Home improvement records		Keep on hand for at least 6 years after sale of home.
Home purchase documents		Keep on hand for at least 6 years after sale of home.
Investment property records		Keep on hand for at least 6 years after sale of property.
Plane, boat, and RV documents		Keep on hand for at least 6 years after sale of property.
Real estate deed		Keep on hand for at least 6 years after sale of property.

Document	Location	How Long to Keep
Time-share/vacation club records		Keep on hand for at least 6 years after sale of property.
Undeveloped land records		Keep on hand for at least 6 years after sale of property.
Vacation home deed and records		Keep on hand for at least 6 years after sale of property.
Other real estate documents		Varies

INCOME

Document	Location	How Long to Keep
Business income statements		Keep for 6 years
Employee benefits summary		Forever
Employee handbook		Forever
Employment agreement		Forever
Investment income statements		Keep for 6 years
Online sales records		Keep for 6 years
Pay stubs		Keep for 6 years
Retirement income statements		Keep for 6 years
Royalty payment statements		Keep for 6 years
Second job documents		Keep for 6 years
Spending account records		Keep for 6 years
Other income documents		Keep for 6 years

DEBTS, LOANS, TAXES, AND EXPENSES

Document	Location	How Long to Keep
Business (commercial property) loan documents		Until updated or paid off (though keep indefinitely as proof of payoff)
Car loan documents		Until updated or paid off (though keep indefinitely as proof of payoff)
Child care and day care documents		Keep until service is canceled.
Club statements		Until account is terminated
Credit card statements and documents		If used for tax purposes, keep for 6 years; otherwise shred statements & receipts after reconciling statement, or longer if you wish to return something.
Debt consolidation loans		Until updated or paid off (though keep indefinitely as proof of payoff)

Continued on next page . . .

Document	Location	How Long to Keep
Education (tuition payments)		Keep until canceled (or if tax-deductible, keep for 6 years after cancellation)
Home loan (mortgage) documents		Until updated or paid off (though keep indefinitely as proof of payoff)
Investment property loans		Until updated or paid off (though keep indefinitely as proof of payoff)
Membership statements		Until account is terminated
Personal loans		Until updated or paid off (though keep indefinitely as proof of payoff)
Private mortgage insurance documents		Until updated or paid off (though keep indefinitely as proof of payoff)
Rental agreements		Retain for up to 6 years after agreement is terminated
Reverse mortgage documents		Until updated or paid off (though keep indefinitely as proof of payoff)
Season ticket documents		If used for tax purposes, keep for 6 years; otherwise shred statements & receipts after reconciling statement, or longer if you wish to return something.
Student loan records		Until updated or paid off (though keep indefinitely as proof of payoff)
Subscription and services documents		Until account is terminated
Tax records		Seven years from filing date
Time-share and vacation club loan documents		Until updated or paid off (though keep indefinitely as proof of payoff)
Utility agreements and statements		Until account is terminated
Vacation home loan documents		Until updated or paid off (though keep indefinitely as proof of payoff)
Other expense documents		Varies

INSURANCE

Document	Location	How Long to Keep
Auto insurance policy and documents		Until coverage ends or is canceled
Disability insurance policy and documents		Until coverage ends or is canceled
Health (and Medicare) insurance policy and documents		Until coverage ends or is canceled
Homeowners and renters insurance policy and documents		Until coverage ends or is canceled

Document	Location	How Long to Keep
Life insurance policy and documents		Until coverage ends or is canceled
Long term care (LTC) insurance policy and documents		Until coverage ends or is canceled
Annuity contracts and statements		Until the contract ends or is canceled
Other insurance policy and documents		Varies

ESTATE PLANNING

Document	Location	How Long to Keep
Digital estate plan		Until updated
Estate plan		Until updated
Final arrangement documents		Until updated
Health care directive/advanced directive		Until updated
Organ and body donation documents		Until updated
Power of attorney		Until updated
Trust(s)		Until updated
Will		Until updated
Other estate planning documents		

NEXT STEPS

As you go through this planner, these documents will be covered in further detail. Until you've completed the planner, you should keep originals of important, irreplaceable documents in a secure location, such as a fireproof safe or safe-deposit box. Copies should go in the GET READY! binder. Add a copy of this list to the Creating Your Financial First Aid Kit section of your GET READY! binder. When you have a new agreement or account, be sure to update this table.

Note

Some of the documents above have recommendations for when you may be able to safely purge a specific item. If there is no purge date, you'll probably want to keep that document forever or use your best judgment on how long to keep it. Personally, I keep items in files for seven years for any closed account with all of my tax documentations, and after seven years, I destroy the physical documents. With the ability to scan documents, I keep digital copies forever. All purged documents should be shredded to help prevent identity theft. Please note that these are just recommendations and are not legal or tax advice. You may wish to seek expert advice if you have concerns about purging a document.

Critical Emergency Action List

Disasters happen and can come in many forms, including floods, wildfires, hurricanes, and earthquakes. If you have to evacuate your home or are concerned about the safety of your home, you may need to move quickly.

In **Table 3,** you can add details about items that are critical to take care of in the event of an emergency, or that a trusted relative, neighbor, or friend can use if you are not home.

Table 3: Critical Emergency Action List

	Location	Details
GET READY! planner and binder location		
Keys: residence, cars, garage, storage, other		
Lock combinations		
Burglar alarm location, code, company, phone number, and secret phrase or other identifier		
Meeting location for your family in the event of an emergency (primary and secondary)		
Water shutoff valve		
Gas shutoff valve		
Main switch to house (fuse box)		
Fire extinguishers		
USB drive and/or portable hard drive		
Photo albums		
Emergency first aid kit & supplies		
Other		
Notes:		

NEXT STEPS

Keep a copy of this list in an easy-to-find location such as on your refrigerator. Also, keep a copy in the Creating Your Financial First Aid Kit section of your GET READY! binder. Consider giving a copy (or partial copy) to a trusted relative, friend, or neighbor.

Contents of Wallet

It's a good idea to make a list of items that you carry in your wallet so that in the event it is lost or stolen, you can immediately cancel all credit/debit cards and replace the contents. Also, if you have a medical emergency, first responders will look through your wallet for identification, health information, and health insurance cards.

In **Table 4**, make a list of everything in your wallet.

Table 4: Contents of Wallet

Item	Notes
Driver's license and/or identification card	
Auto insurance card	
Health insurance card	
Prescription medication card	
Credit cards	
Debit cards	
Membership cards	
Other	
Notes:	

NEXT STEPS

Make a photocopy of each item in your wallet to keep with your secure documents and add copies to the Creating Your Financial First Aid Kit section of your GET READY! binder.

Tip

Do not carry your Social Security card in your wallet. Instead, keep it in a safe place so that it cannot be used for identity theft purposes.

Storing Documents and Valuables

A safe and a safe-deposit box (usually located at a bank) are great for storing documents and valuables. However, if no one knows you have them, the valuable items you store could end up staying safe and unclaimed for a long time before they eventually make their way to your state's unclaimed property department. So be sure to share the location of your valuables with your loved ones. Also, making a list will help you keep track of what's in your safe and/or safe-deposit box.

If you have a safe and/or safe-deposit box, please complete **Table 5** below. Note: In this and many other tables, the * symbol identifies specific items you will need to use in the "Next steps" segment that follows.

Table 5: Storing Documents and Valuables

	Safe	Safe-Deposit Box
Location (for safe-deposit box include name of institution & address)		
Combination for safe		
Location of key(s)		
Description of key (color or other identifier)		
Safe-deposit box number		
Authorized persons for access to box		
Location of safe-deposit box agreement*		
Items stored in box or inventory location*		
Notes:		

> ***NEXT STEPS**
>
> Store your original safe-deposit box agreement with your other secure documents, including an inventory of the items stored in your safe or safe-deposit box. Add a copy of the safe-deposit box agreement to the Creating Your Financial First Aid Kit section of your GET READY! binder.

Storage Unit

A storage unit is a great place to store items that you may not have room for in your home. It's important to document the details regarding your storage unit so that your loved ones will be able to access it.

In **Table 6,** you can add details about your storage unit.

Table 6: Storage Unit

Name of storage facility	
Address & phone number	
Unit number	
Key location (description) and/or lock combination	
Location of documents*	
Inventory of contents*	
Notes:	

*NEXT STEPS

Take a photo of each item and store on a secure USB drive with your secure documents, and store copies in your cloud computer account. Store your original storage unit agreement with your other secure documents, including an inventory of the items stored in your storage unit. Add a copy of the storage unit agreement and inventory to the Creating Your Financial First Aid Kit section of your GET READY! binder.

Personal Information

In **Table 7**, you can record all of your background information. Having this information centrally located can come in handy for many situations—such as getting a loan, purchasing insurance, and many other financial transactions.

Table 7: Personal Information

Full legal name	
Nicknames (or other names known as)	
Maiden name (if applicable)	
Legal name change? (If yes, date of change and name of court, city, and state)	
Prefix (Ms., Mr., Dr., etc.)	
Suffix (Jr., Sr., etc.)	
Current home address (date moved in and state, county, and country)	
Previous home address	
Mailing address (if different)	
P.O. box	
Office address	
Current state of legal residence (state in which you vote)	
Home phone	
Work phone	
Mobile phone	
Email addresses (log-in credentials will be added in a later section)	
Personal website	
Date of birth	
Place of birth	
Citizenship (by birth or by naturalization)	

Passport number & expiration date*	
Naturalization documents	
Marital status (single, married, divorced, widowed, separated, domestic partner)	
Spouse/domestic partner name	
Spouse/domestic partner birthday	
Anniversary	
If spouse is deceased, enter date of death and location of remains	
Ex-spouse name	
Marriage date for ex-spouse	
Divorce date for ex-spouse	
Location of divorce papers	
Contact information for ex-spouse (home address, home telephone, cell phone, work phone, and email address)	
Sibling names and contact information	
High school name	
College name and degree	
Other	
Notes:	

*NEXT STEPS

Keep your original passport with your secure documents. Keep a copy of your passport in the Creating Your Financial First Aid Kit section of your GET READY! binder. Enter passport expiration date and other relevant dates on your financial calendar (page 216).

Tip

You can obtain copies of birth, adoption, death, marriage, and divorce certificates from your state health or social services administration office for a minimal fee. The Centers for Disease Control and Prevention (CDC) maintains a state contact list at www.cdc.gov/nchs/w2w.htm.

Passport or green cards: Having a copy of your passport or green card will make obtaining a replacement quicker if needed. Information about applying for renewing a passport is available at www.travel.state.gov/content/passports/english.html. You can also call the National Passport Information Center at (877) 487-2778. Information about applying for, renewing, and replacing a green card is available at www.uscis.gov/greencard.

US Citizenship and Immigration services information is available at www.uscis.gov. Naturalization documents are the only acceptable proof of citizenship for individuals not born in the United States.

Children

Whether your children are still kids or fully grown, they are part of your financial life as you may be financially supporting them, they may be taking care of you, and you may be leaving your estate (or a portion) to them.

In **Table 8**, enter information on all of your children. If you have more than three, please use the Notes section at the end of this chapter.

Table 8: Children

Full name			
Date of birth			
Relationship (son, daughter, step, half, adopted, foster)			
Name of other birth parent			
Place of birth (hospital born in name & city and state)			
Location of child's birth certificate*			
Name of school or day care facility			
Approved person(s) for school/day care pickup			
If child is adopted, list any other name, birth parent names, adoption agency, and adoption document locations			

If foster child, enter related information			
Date of marriage			
If child has passed away, include date of death, cause of death, location of remains			
Notes:			

*NEXT STEPS

Keep your children's original birth certificates with your secure documents. Keep a copy of the birth certificates in the Creating Your Financial First Aid Kit section of your GET READY! binder.

Tip

Be sure to keep your children's identification records, including recent photographs, child identity cards with fingerprints, dental records (typically stored by dental care providers), or DNA swabs. The Federal Bureau of Investigation (FBI) recommends obtaining a kit from the National Child Identification Program (http://www.childidprogram.com).

Grandchildren

Grandchildren are one of the best parts of life. In **Table 9** below, enter basic information about them so that they can be located when they become the beneficiary of a financial asset or when you pass away.

Table 9: Grandchildren

Full legal name (include maiden name)			
Birthdate			
Parent name(s)			
Contact information			
Notes:			

Health (Medical) Information

We all have to visit a medical professional at some point, especially if we follow recommendations by having our annual physical and seeing the dentist twice a year. Keeping track of this information is handy for you and for your caregivers and survivors. **Table 10** will help you enter basic information on your health history.

Table 10: Health History

Primary physician (full name and contact information)	
Date last seen	
Other physicians/specialists/clinics (names and contact information)	
Hospital (preferred, name and address)	
Known medical conditions	
Allergies	
Pharmacy drug store (name and location)	
Medications (name, purpose, Rx #, dosage, dates taken/started)	
Medical devices	
Medications or medical supplies on auto-delivery (name and supplier contact information)	
Blood type	
Vaccinations	
Dentist (name and contact info)	
Optometrist (name and contact info)	
Orthodontist (name and contact info)	
Specialist (name and contact info)	
Immediate family medical history (who, major condition, when diagnosed, age if living, age passed away)	
Notes:	

Note

It's important to retain paper copies of your medical records for two years. You can hold on to digital records indefinitely. It's a good practice to request the results of your lab tests, screenings, and in-office checks such as blood pressure, weight, cholesterol, and even specialized tests like X-rays. Records will include summaries of your visit and details on prescription medications. These can now usually be downloaded from your medical provider's website. You will want to review for accuracy. Having a copy of your records will assist you in applying for other types of insurance that require medical underwriting.

Tip

The DEA provides an online tool to let you find the nearest drop-off site for unused drugs. A link to that page and more information can be found on the DEA's website at https://www.deadiversion.usdoj.gov/drug_disposal/takeback. You can also call (800) 882-9539 for the location of a nearby collection site.

Pet Information

Pets are part of your family. You can use **Table 11** to add information about your pets to facilitate the continuation of their wellness and care in the event of your passing. If you have more than two, you can add information in the Notes section at the end of this chapter.

Table 11: Pets

	Pet 1	Pet 2
Pet name		
Animal type		
Species/breed		
Color		
Sex		

Continued on next page . . .

	Pet 1	Pet 2
Birth date		
License number		
AKC number (pet registry)		
Other ID numbers or unique features		
Veterinarian name (and contact information)		
Health conditions		
Medications (and dosages)		
Vaccinations (and records location)*		
Notes: (breed and groomer info, spayed, neutered, other)		

*NEXT STEPS

Keep vaccination records and other pet papers with your secure documents. Keep a copy of these records in the Creating Your Financial First Aid Kit section of your GET READY! binder.

Tip

Be sure to keep a copy of your pet's ID tag numbers and microchip information. At this time, there is not a central database in the US for registering microchips; each manufacturer maintains its own database (or has it managed by someone else). Because the ISO standards for identification codes have not been adopted in the US, the microchips must be registered with their individual registries. In 2009, the American Animal Hospital Association launched a Universal Pet Microchip Lookup Tool (www.petmicrochiplookup.org), which provides a listing of the manufacturer with which the microchip's code is associated as well as whether or not the chip information can be found in participating registries. The database does not provide owner information for the microchip; the user must contact the manufacturer/database associated with that microchip.

Military Service

Serving one's country is an honorable part of one's life. In **Table 12**, you can add basic information on your military service. It's important to document this information so that you and your family can receive the full financial and medical benefits you've earned.

Table 12: Military Service

Payroll name (first, middle, last)	
Branch (Army, Navy, Air Force, Marines, Coast Guard, National Guard)	
Status (active, reserve, retired, discharged)	
Current rank/final rank	
Military ID #	
Serial # (DD214)	
Veterans Affairs #	
Date entered	
Active duty station	
TDY/PCS orders	
AGR info	
Date discharged/retired/released	
Honors, medals, and citations (and location)	
Location of DD-213	
Location of Common Access Card and number	
Location of Uniformed Services ID Card and number	
Notes:	

NEXT STEPS

Keep original documents, including all orders, with your secure documents and add copies to the Creating Your Financial First Aid Kit section of your GET READY! binder.

Tip

If you have questions or need to replace or manage your Common Access Card or Uniformed Services ID Card, you can go to the Department of Defense ID Card reference center (www.cac.mil). If you are a veteran, you can obtain copies of your DD214 (military discharge form) by contacting the US National Archives and Records Administration at (866) 272-6272 or online at www.archives.gov/veterans.

Memberships: Clubs and Organizations

Actively participating in clubs and organizations can enrich our lives. In **Table 13** below, add information for up to three clubs—including religious, community, or service organizations. Maintaining records of your memberships will help your loved ones make sure that this is included as part of your legacy and that memberships are terminated when you are no longer able to use them. If you've belonged to more, use the Notes section at the end of this chapter.

Table 13: Clubs and Organizations

Name of club/organization			
Address			
Membership #			
Membership level			
Date joined			
Role			
Website and log-in credentials			
Location of documents*			
Notes:			

*NEXT STEPS

Keep original documents and orders with your secure documents and add copies to the Creating Your Financial First Aid Kit section of your GET READY! binder.

Charitable Organizations

People choose to support charities, nonprofits, and other organizations in a variety of ways, with one of the most common being that of volunteering. In **Table 14**, list any charitable organizations that you volunteer with.

Table 14: Charitable Organizations

Name of charity/nonprofit			
Address			
Date started			
Role			
Website and log-in credentials			
Location of documents*			
Notes:			

*NEXT STEPS

Keep original documents with your secure documents and add copies to the Creating Your Financial First Aid Kit section of your GET READY! binder.

Digital Life (Devices and Services)

Technology has changed our lives in many positive ways. This digital life can be broken down into two parts: the physical devices that we have and the online services that we use. In the digital estate planning section on page 187, you can make a note of what should happen to devices and services in the event of your death.

In **Table 15**, enter the requested information about your devices. Noting the model number and serial number will help you document any insurance claims. This information will help your loved ones be able to use your devices.

Table 15: Digital Life

Device	Description	Location	Model Number	Serial Number	Password	PIN
Cell phone 1						
Cell phone 2						
Computer/ laptop						
Tablet						
Other						
Other						

NEXT STEPS

Keep original sales receipts and warranties with your secure documents. Add copies of sales receipts to the Creating Your Financial First Aid Kit section of your GET READY! binder.

Tracking Your Log-In Credentials

The internet has given us many great online services, from convenient banking to cloud storage. The downside is that we have a lot of user names and passwords to keep track of. Recording this information is important so that your loved ones can access your accounts if needed.

In **Table 16**, you can enter your log-in credentials so that all of your online services can be accessed easily in the event a loved one needs to step in on your behalf. (Websites that are affiliated with a paid service or are for an account, such as a bank account or car loan, will be covered later in this planner.) If you have more accounts than can fit in this table or elsewhere in this planner, please download the worksheet from www.tonysteuer.com/resources or create a spreadsheet of your own to reference.

Table 16: Log-In Credentials

Service/ Website	Website	Email Affiliated with Account	User Name	Password	Secret Question(s)
PASSWORD MANAGER					
Email 1					
Email 2					
Email 3					
Blog 1					
Blog 2					
Website 1					
Website 2					
CLOUD STORAGE					
Box					
Dropbox					
Google Drive					
iCloud					
Microsoft OneDrive					
SugarSync					
Other					

Continued on next page . . .

Service/ Website	Website	Email Affiliated with Account	User Name	Password	Secret Question(s)
COMMUNICATION SERVICES					
Kik					
Skype					
WhatsApp					
FINANCIAL SERVICES					
Google Wallet					
LearnVest					
PayPal					
Venmo					
WePay					
GAMING					
Battle.net					
Nintendo					
Xbox Live					
PlaySta- tion Plus					
Steam					
MUSIC ACCOUNTS					
iTunes					
Lastfm					
Spotify					
Pandora					
Rdio					
Other					

Service/ Website	Website	Email Affiliated with Account	User Name	Password	Secret Question(s)

SOCIAL MEDIA

Facebook					
Instagram					
LinkedIn					
Pinterest					
Snapchat					
Twitter					
Other					

SHOPPING

Amazon					
Best Buy					
eBay					
Etsy					
Target					
Walmart					
Travel 1					
Travel 2					
OpenTable					
Yelp					
Other					
Notes:					

Continued on next page . . . ➡

NEXT STEPS

Add a copy of this worksheet to your secure documents. You can also keep a copy in Creating Your Financial First Aid Kit section of your GET READY! binder.

Reward and Loyalty Programs

Businesses encourage people to continue to use their product or service. These programs come in many forms and are usually known as reward programs or loyalty programs. Most of us will have more than we can keep track of. Some reward and loyalty programs such as a frequent flyer program will allow you to pass on your miles to a loved one.

In **Table 17**, you can enter the name of the company and/or program, your account number, the website, and log-in credentials. Having this information handy will help you in the event you need the information for yourself or your loved ones to take advantage of unused rewards.

Table 17: Loyalty Programs

Company	Program Name	Account #	Website	User Name	Password	Secret Questions
Airline 1						
Airline 2						
Airline 3						
Hotel 1						
Hotel 2						
Hotel 3						
Rental car 1						
Rental car 2						
Other						
Notes						

END-OF-CHAPTER CHECK-IN

Did this chapter help you GET READY!? In **Table 18**, assess your level of financial preparedness by checking the appropriate status box for all the topics in this chapter.

Table 18: End-of-Chapter Check-In

	In Progress	Completed	Not Applicable
Emergency contact list			
Personal papers & legal documents master list			
Critical emergency action list			
Contents of wallet			
Storing documents and valuables			
Personal information			
Children			
Grandchildren			
Health information (medical)			
Pet information			
Military service			
Memberships: clubs and organizations			
Charitable organizations			
Digital life (devices and services)			
Reward and loyalty programs			

PRINT FORMS

To print these forms, visit my website at www.tonysteuer.com/resources.

NOTES

CHAPTER 3

Listing Your Assets

Price is what you pay. Value is what you get.
—WARREN BUFFETT

Carrying around the latest, most advanced first aid supplies, such as an AED defibrillator, suture kit, or blood pressure cuff, won't help you if you are not familiar with what they are and how to use them. Without this knowledge, these just become excess baggage. In this chapter we're going to take the time to understand what you own and how these assets can work for you.

 GET READY!: ORGANIZING YOUR NON-RETIREMENT ASSETS

In this chapter, we will be reviewing your liquid assets—money you could access quickly and easily if you needed to. Assets that are not liquid, such as retirement accounts or property, will be covered in the chapters that follow. While organizing this part of the planner, you will learn about—

1. **Bank accounts.** You will be making a list of all of your savings and checking accounts and CDs. You'll also record information on the accounts themselves, along with the balances.

2. **Marketable securities and investments.** You'll make an inventory of all of your stocks, bonds, mutual funds, and exchange-traded funds—basically, everything that can be sold quickly and easily at any time.

3. **Business interests.** You will also document the value of any business that you own, whether you are a consultant working for yourself, a partner in a law firm, or an owner of a large business.

4. **College savings accounts.** You'll gather information on college savings account plans that you've put in place to help your children, grandchildren, or others who need funding for higher education costs.

5. **ABLE accounts.** This is a new type of account for children and young adults living with disabilities. If this applies to you, you'll want to include this in your planner as well.

Managing your money entails saving your money as well as investing it. You'll also want to have some money available to meet short-term needs while you put aside other money for the long term. Usually, the longer-term your goal is, such as retirement, the less liquid (accessible) your money has to be.

Checking and Savings Accounts

Bank accounts allow you to deposit and withdraw money while sometimes being paid interest. Checking and savings accounts form the foundation of your assets. Both provide a safe place to put your money and will help you start saving. Checking accounts allow you to make deposits, withdrawals, and transfers, as well as write checks. There are even some that pay interest. You will usually be provided with a debit or ATM card along with a checkbook. A savings account is an interest-earning deposit account and will usually pay a higher interest rate than a checking account.

On the facing page, you can add details regarding your checking, savings, or other bank accounts to **Table 19**. You can find this information on your bank statements or online. If you have more than one account, use the second column. The tables that follow in this planner include an entry line labeled "As of date." This date shows when you originally entered the information, and lets you know whether it's current or out of date.

Note

A money market account is a type of savings account that can earn a higher interest rate than a traditional savings account. Usually you can write a limited number of checks with this account, which is backed by the FDIC. Note that there are also money market "funds," which are subject to market fluctuations and are not FDIC-insured.

Managing Your Fees and Expenses: This is one of the best things you can do for your investment portfolio. If you can save 1 percent on your annual fees and expenses, that is an additional 1 percent gain for your portfolio. This is often easier said than done, as many fees and expenses are not clearly disclosed or easy to understand. If you can't understand something, you shouldn't buy it.

Advisory Costs: If you are using a financial planner or other advisor to help you with your investments, you are most likely paying a percentage of your assets as a management fee. And this is with fee-based planners. If you are working with an advisor who also receives commissions or other compensation, you are also paying for that—either directly or indirectly. It's important to ask how your advisor is compensated.

Cost Basis: This is the price you paid for an asset, plus or minus any tax adjustments, commissions, or fees. In the case of stocks or mutual funds, your cost basis would be what you paid for the shares, plus any commissions.

Ownership: There are many types of ownership, and it is important to understand these different types and how they affect your assets. Common types of ownership include joint tenants with rights of survivorship, joint tenants in the entirety, individual, transfer/payable on death, and tenants in common.

Table 19: Checking and Savings Accounts

Type of account (checking, savings, money market, other)		
Institution and branch location		
Account number(s)		
Owners of account/titling		
Ownership type		
As of date		
Account value*		
Interest rate		
Interest amount* (or dividend)		
ATM card number		
ATM/debit card location		
ATM PIN		
Beneficiary		
Automatic deposits to account (payor, contact info, how often, amount)		
Automatic payments from account (payee, contact info, how often, amount)		
Monthly service fee(s)		
Minimum balance charge(s)		
Overdraft fee(s)		
ATM fees		
Other fees and charges		
How statements are sent? (if email, note email address)		
Location of checks, any used checkbooks and/or savings books, along with account documentation		
Website address and log-in credentials		
Notes:		

Continued on next page . . . ➡

Tip

Manage your checking and savings accounts. It's important to review your account statements to avoid unnecessary fees and to make sure that transactions are correct. You'll also want to check your statements to catch any fraudulent activity. Reconciling your checking account with the monthly statement will help you stay on track. Consider reviewing options at different institutions to save or eliminate fees and earn higher interest rates.

It's important to look around for an account that will meet your needs. There are many sites on the internet that allow you to compare bank account options. It's also important to verify that you have deposit insurance, which provides guarantees up to a specific amount, in the event your bank goes under. Banks should be members of the Federal Deposit Insurance Corporation (FDIC) (http://research.fdic.gov/bankfind), and credit unions can participate in the National Credit Union Insurance Fund (NCUSIF) (http://www.ncua.gov/dataapps/pages/si-ncua.aspx).

Certificates of Deposit (CDs)

A certificate of deposit, commonly known as a CD, is traditionally a deposit-only account that has a guaranteed interest rate for a specific period of time. The term (time period) is usually 6, 12, 18, or 60 months. The longer the period, the higher the annual percentage rate. If you decided to withdraw your money before the end of the term, you would have to pay an early withdrawal penalty, and the bank has the right to deny the request for early withdrawals. Therefore, it's really important to consider if locking up your money is worth a higher interest rate. There are other types of CDs, so be sure that you understand what you are purchasing, and what the withdrawal penalties are, and make sure that the bank is FDIC insured.

Please enter information about any CDs you own in **Table 20**. This information can be found on the original CD paperwork or on any statement. If you have more than one CD, use the second column.

Table 20: Certificates of Deposit

Institution		
Account number		
Owners of account/titling		

Name of any joint account owner		
Effective date		
Maturity date*		
Term period		
Interest rate		
As of date		
Fair market value*		
Withdrawal penalties		
Beneficiary		
How statements are sent (if email, record email address)		
Location of certificate(s) and account documents		
Website and log-in credentials		
Notes:		

*NEXT STEPS

From the table, enter your account value in the assets section on your net worth statement (page 199). Add the maturity date to your financial calendar (page 216). Store your CD paperwork with your secure documents and add a summary or statement (if available) to the assets section of your GET READY! binder.

Tip

When your CD's term period ends, it is called "maturing," and you will have the option to place your money elsewhere or to reinvest or "roll" your money into a new CD. Usually banks will automatically roll your funds into a new CD with the same time period, unless you tell them not to. It's always good to check with your financial institution to find out what their policy is.

Stocks

A stock is an instrument that provides the holder with an ownership interest "equity" in a corporation and a claim on the proportional share of the corporation's assets and profits. Stocks usually also have voting rights, which give shareholders a proportional vote in certain corporate decisions. Keep in mind that major corporations will have millions of shares of stock, so your 1,000 shares are a drop in the bucket.

There are other types of stock, including preferred stock. Preferred stock has a higher claim on assets and earnings than common stock, though it does not have voting rights. Preferred stock also entitles the holder to a fixed dividend and is generally considered a hybrid investment.

In **Table 21**, enter information on your stock holdings. You can enter information on a summary basis for your stock portfolio or on individual stocks. You can find this information on account statements or online. If you have more than one stock, use the second column.

Table 21: Stocks

Company		
Ticker symbol		
Where is stock held? (brokerage name and account #) Or do you have a certificate?		
Type (common, preferred, convertible, other)		
Certificate number		
Date acquired		
Number of shares		
Cost basis		
Share price		
As of date		
Total current value (multiply # of shares by current share price)*		
Estimated gain or loss (subtract cost basis from total value)		
Annual dividend per share		
Annual dividend total (multiply number of shares by dividend per share)*		
Dividend yield (annual dividend per share divided by price per share)		

Dividend payout date		
Class of stock (common, preferred, other)		
If stock is preferred, is stock convertible? If so, include date for conversion		
Ownership		
Market capitalization		
Industry and sector		
Type of stock (growth, value, other)		
Has there been a stock split or reverse split? Insert split ratio and date(s)		
Stock location (document)		
Website address and log-in credentials		
Notes:		

*NEXT STEPS

From the table, add dividends to the income section of your cash flow statement (page 193). Enter the total current value in the assets section of your net worth statement (page 199). Store original stock certificates and documentation with your secure documents and add a current brokerage statement to the assets section of your GET READY! binder.

Track the following to ensure that you have a diversified investment portfolio:

- **Market capitalization:** This describes the company's size. Companies are commonly referred to as large-cap, mid-cap, and small-cap. It's the dollar value of the company, or number of outstanding shares multiplied by the current market price.
- **Industry and sector:** Sectors are large sections of the economy, such as industrial companies, financial companies, or utility companies. Industries are a subset of sectors. For example, insurance companies are an industry that is part of the financial sector. Sectors and industries can have their own cycles that are different from the overall market.
- **Growth and value:** Companies are usually either growth stocks, where the company is expanding, or value stocks for established companies that aren't growing. While growth stocks are almost always new companies, they can also include companies that have been around for a while. Although value stocks tend to represent companies that aren't growing, they may prove to have exceptional value in that they may be underpriced.

Bonds

Bonds are a loan from the bondholder to the issuer of the bond. You invest in the bond, then, at its maturity date, you get back the face value of the bond. Bond maturities can vary and may be classified as "short-term" (under 3 years), "intermediate" (3–9 years), or "long-term" (over 9 years). Bonds can be issued by companies or by governments at all levels (federal/treasury, state, and municipal). Bonds usually pay a fixed interest rate and are considered safer investments than stocks, though there are some bonds that can be high risk.

BOND TERMS

- **Coupon rate:** This is the interest rate paid by the bond. In most cases, it won't change after the bond is issued.
- **Discount rate:** This is the amount by which the auction price of a marketable security is lower than its face value.
- **Face value:** This is the amount the bond is worth when it's issued, also known as "par value." Most bonds have a face value of $1,000.
- **Maturity:** This refers to the length of time until you receive the bond's face value (or maturity date).
- **Price:** This is the amount the bond would currently cost on the secondary market. Several factors play into a bond's current price, but one of the biggest is how favorable its coupon rate and/or yield is compared with other similar bonds.
- **Quality:** Bonds are rated on the issuer's current financial and credit histories by third-party agencies such as Standard & Poor's and Moody's Investors Service. If a bond's rating is very high, the yield will be lower, as you are relatively certain to receive payments and the face value. If the bond is considered "below investment grade," you should expect a higher yield, as it will have a higher risk level for receiving all payments and the face value at maturity.
- **Yield:** This is a measure of interest that takes into account the bond's fluctuating changes in value. There are different ways to measure yield, but the simplest is the coupon of the bond divided by the current price.
- **Callable bonds:** These allow the issuer to retire a bond before it matures. Call provisions are outlined in the bond's prospectus (or offering statement) and the indenture.

Treasury Securities (Bills and Bonds)

Treasury securities are debts issued by the US government and can be bought directly through www .treasurydirect.gov or through a third party.

On the facing page, enter information on any Treasury securities in **Table 22**. This information can be found on recent statements or online. If you have more than one Treasury security, use the second column.

Table 22: Treasury Securities (Bills and Bonds)

Institution/Treasury direct account		
Account number		
Ownership/titling		
Type		
As of date		
Face value (par)		
Current price (value)*		
Issue date		
Maturity date(s)		
Discount rate		
Yield		
Cost basis		
How statements are received (email, mail)		
Documents location		
Website with log-in credentials		
Notes:		

*NEXT STEPS

From the table above, enter the annual yield in the income section of your cash flow statement (page 193). Enter the current price (value) in the assets section of your net worth statement (page 199). Add the maturity date to your financial calendar (page 216). Store your paperwork with your secure documents and add a summary or statement to the assets section of your GET READY! binder.

TREASURY SECURITIES

Treasury securities can be purchased online through treasurydirect.gov or through a bank or broker. Following are the different types of Treasury securities:

- **Treasury bills:** These are short-term securities that mature between a few days and 52 weeks. The difference between the purchase price and the face value is interest (there is no other interest paid). These can be considered as a cash equivalent.

- **Treasury notes:** These are medium-term securities that have maturity dates of 2, 3, 5, 7, and 10 years. These pay interest every 6 months.
- **Treasury bonds:** These are long-term securities, with 10- to 30-year terms (maturities), that pay interest every 6 months, until the bond matures.
- **Treasury inflation-protected securities (TIPS):** These are marketable securities whose principal value is adjusted every 6 months by changes in the Consumer Price Index that have terms of 5, 10, and 30 years. Interest is fixed and is paid every 6 months. At maturity you are paid the adjusted principal or original principal (whichever is greater).
- **Floating rate notes (FRNs):** Issued for a term of two years, FRNs pay varying amounts of interest quarterly until maturity. Interest payments rise and fall based on discount rates in auctions of 13-week Treasury bills.
- **Series I savings bonds**: While you own them, they earn interest and protect you from inflation by having an interest rate derived from a fixed rate and a semi-annual inflation rate. Interest, if any, is added to the bond monthly and is paid when you cash the bond. Series I bonds are sold at face value with a minimum term of 1 year and an interest-earning period of 30 years. If you redeem before 5 years, you will forfeit the 3 most recent months of interest.
- **Series EE savings bonds**: You will earn interest for up to 30 years on these bonds. Any issued after 2005 earn a fixed interest rate, which is added to the EE bond monthly and paid when you cash the bond. Bonds are sold at face value with a minimum term of 1 year and an interest-earning period of 30 years. If you redeem before 5 years, you will forfeit the 3 most recent months of interest.

Corporate Bonds, Government Agency Bonds, and Municipal Bonds

In **Table 23**, enter information regarding any bonds you own. You may enter information about individual bonds or a summary of your total bond portfolio. You can locate the information from either an account statement or online. If you have more than one, use the second column.

Table 23: Corporate Bonds, Government Agency Bonds, and Municipal Bonds

Bond (full name)		
Issuing entity (name of corporation, government, federal agency, or other organization)		
Account number		
Where held/located		
Ownership (how title is held)		
Bond series		

Date acquired		
Number of bonds		
Face value (par amount)		
Unit price paid		
Total price paid (basis)		
As of date		
Current price per unit		
Coupon rate		
Discount rate		
Maturity date		
Yield (coupon of the bond divided by the current price)		
Total current value*		
Annual coupon amount*		
Gain (loss)		
Quality from Standard & Poor's or Moody's (bond rating)		
Is the bond callable? If yes, what are provisions?		
Location of documents		
Website address and log-in credentials		
Notes:		

*NEXT STEPS

From the table above, enter the annual yield in the income section of your cash flow statement (page 193). Enter the current price (value) in the assets section of your net worth statement (page 199). Store your paperwork with your secure documents and add a summary or statement to the assets section of your GET READY! binder.

Tip

There are many types of bonds. Here are some common types:

- **Corporate bonds**: Corporate bonds are issued by companies that are backed by their corporate assets. Interest from these bonds is subject to federal and state income taxes. Credit ratings vary widely, which impacts yield. Yields are higher than government bonds because they are not as safe. High-yield (junk) bonds are corporate bonds with low credit ratings.

- **Government agency bonds:** Certain US government agencies can issue bonds. This includes housing-related agencies like the Government National Mortgage Association (GNMA or Ginnie Mae). These bonds are typically high-quality and very liquid, although yields may not keep pace with inflation. Some agency bonds are fully backed by the US government, while others are not. Agency bonds are taxable at the federal and state level.

- **Municipal bonds:** Municipal bonds, also referred to as "munis" or "muni bonds," are issued by state or local government agencies. They are generally considered safe because the issuer has the ability to raise money through taxes, though there is a possibility the issuer could default. Interest is free from federal income tax, as well as state tax in the state of issue. Yields are usually lower than bonds that are subject to federal income tax.

Note

Bonds with longer maturities have a greater level of risk due to changes in interest rates. They generally offer higher yields, so they're more attractive to potential buyers. The relationship between maturity and yield is called the yield curve. In a normal yield curve, shorter maturities equal lower yield.

Mutual Funds

A mutual fund is a pool of investments that can be used in retirement and non-retirement accounts. They are often defined as being for stocks; however, there are also mutual funds for bonds, foreign currency, precious metals, real estate, and other investment vehicles. Mutual funds provide the following benefits:

- Increased diversification

- Lower transaction costs

- Easier record-keeping

Prospectuses and annual reports are used to disclose holdings along with objectives, risks, costs, and other details. Key details that can be used in reviewing alternatives, such as share values, historical returns, and fund holdings, can be found online or through investment advisors. A good resource for information is www.morningstar.com.

In **Table 24**, you can enter information about your mutual funds either in summary or individually. This information can be found on your account statements or online. If you have more than one mutual fund, use the second column.

Table 24: Mutual Funds

Mutual fund (full name)		
Investment company		
Entity where mutual fund is held		
Account number(s)		
Ownership titling		
Date acquired		
Number of shares		
Price paid per share		
Cost basis (total price paid)		
Current price per share		
Total current value*		
As of date		
Gain (loss)		
Dividends*		
Share class (A, B or C)		
Expense ratio		
Tax cost ratio		
Location of documents		
Website and log-in credentials		
Notes:		

Continued on next page . . . ➡

Note

Mutual funds will vary in terms of management style, steady or fluctuating returns, expenses and fees, volatility, and safety, among other trade-offs, so it's important to understand if a fund matches your investment goals and risk tolerance.

Exchange-Traded Funds (ETFs)

An exchange-traded fund (ETF) is a basket of securities that you can buy or sell through a brokerage firm on a stock exchange. ETFs are offered on virtually every conceivable asset class, from traditional investments to so-called alternative assets like commodities or currencies. In addition, innovative ETF structures allow investors to short markets, to gain leverage, and to avoid short-term capital gains taxes.

In **Table 25**, you can enter information about your ETFs either in summary or individually. This information can be found on your account statements or online. If you have more than one ETF, use the second column.

Table 25: Exchange-Traded Funds

ETF (full name)		
Investment company		
Ticker symbol		
Account number		
Entity where ETF is held		
Titling (ownership)		
Date acquired		
Number of shares		
Price paid (per share)		

Total price paid (cost basis)		
As of date		
Current price per share		
Total current value*		
Gain (loss)		
Expense ratio		
Class		
Location of documents		
Website and log-in credentials		
Notes:		

*NEXT STEPS

From the table above, enter any annual dividends in the income section of your cash flow statement (page 193). Enter the current value in the assets section of your net worth statement (page 199). Keep the original documents with your secure documents and add a recent statement to the assets section of your GET READY! binder.

Note

ETFs can be bought or sold at any time of day, and the price will vary during the day, whereas mutual funds settle after the market closes. ETFs have low expense charges and no sales load. The number of shares will change daily as new shares are sold and existing shares are redeemed. It's this constant issuing of new shares and redeeming of existing shares that keep ETFs in line with the value of their underlying securities. ETF sales are settled three days after the transaction, which limits your access to the funds.

Collectibles

Collectibles include investments in certain assets that have value, such as art, collectibles, gold coins, jewelry, rare stamps, and any other investment property that you have not already listed in this planner. Collectibles are considered an investment because you have purchased them with the intention of reselling them for a profit at some time in the future.

In **Table 26**, list your collectibles and pertinent details. If you have a specific inventory tool for your collectibles, you can take total values from there and add the location of that tracking spreadsheet.

Table 26: Collectibles

Asset (collectible name)		
Description		
Titling (ownership)		
Date(s) acquired		
Value at acquisition (cost basis)		
Current value (appraised or researched opinion)*		
Most recent appraisal date		
Appraiser name(s) and contact info		
Certificate of authenticity (yes/no)		
Location of documents		
Notes:		

*NEXT STEPS

From the table above, enter the total value of your collectibles in the assets section of your net worth statement (page 199). Store certificates of authenticity, appraisals, and other documents in a secure location. You can also add a summary of your collectibles to the assets section of your GET READY! binder.

Stock Options

Stock options allow the holder to buy or sell a fixed amount of a given stock at a specified price within a limited time period. Stock options (SO) can be purchased or they can be provided to employees. When awarded to employees as regular stock options (RSOs) or non-qualified stock options (NQSOs), they may be subject to income taxes at the time the option is granted if the option price is less than the fair market value; this difference is considered taxable compensation. There are also incentive stock options provided through an employee stock option plan that grants key employees options to purchase company stock at a predetermined price without incurring a tax liability, either at the time the option is granted or when exercised.

You can use **Table 27** to enter information on any stock options you may have. You can enter individual options or a summary of all of your options. If you are receiving options through your employer, they will often provide a summary that can be used to update your planner. If you have more than one set of options, use the second column.

Table 27: Stock Options

Title of stock option		
Description		
Type of stock option (SO, RSO, NQSO)		
Date(s) granted		
Number of stock options		
Option price per share (when granted)		
Current value per share		
Current total value (multiply current value per share by number of option shares)*		
Option value(s) (multiply option price per share by number of option shares)		
Current gain/loss—bargain element (option value less market value)		
As of date		
Date or time period during which stock options may be exercised*		
Expiration date of options*		
If trading options, enter name of platform and details to access account (website and log-in credentials)		
Location of documents		
Notes:		

Continued on next page . . .

Note

The value for non-publicly traded stock can come from an estimated value based on your knowledge of the company.

Business Interests/Ownerships

Part of the American dream is to be your own boss. Past studies have shown that 57 percent of Americans would prefer to own their own business or at least be self-employed. Around 14 percent actually run their own business. It is common in certain occupations to have the opportunity to be a partner, which means there is an ownership interest.

In **Table 28**, enter basic information on a business in which you have an ownership interest. If you have more than one business, you can enter information in the Notes section at the end of the chapter.

Table 28: Business Interest/Ownership

Business name (full legal name)	
Definition of business (what it does)	
Type of business (sole proprietor, partnership, LLC, LLP, C-Corp, S-Corp, other)	
How title is held	
Percentage of business ownership interest	
Partner(s) or co-owner(s) and contact information	
Position in company	
Tax identification number	
Cost basis (amount paid in for your interest) —for partnerships, this can be found on your form K-1	
Date interest acquired or that you started the business	

Current value of your interest*	
As of date	
Number of shares owned	
Class of shares/breakdown (example: Class A: 50%, Class B: 50%)	
Details on what happens to business if you become disabled or die	
Business advisor names and contact information	
Business bank account and credit card (bank/lender name, account #)	
Location of inventory	
Location of documents and agreements	
Notes:	

*NEXT STEPS

Add the current value of your business interest to the assets section of your net worth statement (page 199). Keep original documents with your secure documents and add copies to the assets section of your GET READY! binder.

Note

The value of non-public business can be estimated from offers to buy, the value of comparable companies, your buy-sell agreement, or your partners' or advisors' opinions.

Royalties (Copyrights, Trademarks, Patents, and Other Property That Can Be Licensed)

If you have created something, whether it's a book, music, a work of art, or a better mousetrap, you will usually receive some type of royalty payment on your creation. Royalties can be paid out for perpetuity (forever) or for a limited time period.

In **Table 29**, enter details on any copyrights, trademarks, patents, or other properties for which you receive a royalty. If you have more than one work for which you receive royalties, use the second column.

Table 29: Royalties (Copyrights, Trademarks, Patents, and Other Property That Can Be Licensed)

Name of property		
Description of property		
Copyright, trademark, or patent		
Registration number		
Date granted		
Termination date		
Value (if any)*		
As of date		
How often distributed		
Distribution amount*		
When filed		
Status		
Location of documents		
Notes:		

*NEXT STEPS

From the table above, enter the distribution amount in the income section of your cash flow statement (page 193). Add the total value, if any, to the assets section of your net worth statement (page 199) . Enter the termination date on your financial calendar (page 216). Keep your original documentation with your secure documents. If you have a summary or recent royalty statement, add it to the assets section of your GET READY! binder.

Debts and Obligations Owed to You (Loans You Have Made)

A loan directly to a family member is less risky than being a co-signer on a loan with them. As a co-signer, you would be responsible if the other party defaults, and it would go on your credit record. If you make a private loan, you should have a written agreement to protect both you as the lender and the borrower, which makes it a formal transaction. The agreement should list the terms of the loan, the amount of the loan, and the interest rate. Loans can also be made through an online service such as Kiva or the Lending Club. These services generally have detailed reporting capabilities, and you should maintain all reports.

You can summarize the total loan balances below along with any private loans in **Table 30**, which follows. If you have more than one debt or loan owed to you, use the second column.

Table 30: Debts and Obligations Owed to You (Loans Made by You)

Type of loan		
Debtor/servicer (website)		
Debtor contact info		
Originating date		
Loan maturity (end) date		
Amount borrowed		
Current balance owed*		
As of date		
Payment amount & frequency*		
Interest rate		
Website and log-in credentials, if applicable		
Loan documentation		
Notes:		

Continued on next page . . . ➥

Note

Be aware that the IRS requires details if the loan exceeds a specified amount and that the lender must charge interest of at least the IRS-approved applicable federal rate (AFR), which changes monthly and varies by the length of the loan period. If the AFR is not charged and the loan exceeds the annual gift tax exemption, the lender will be required to pay gift taxes, unless the borrower agrees to pay the gift tax (the gift tax can be as much as 40 percent).

College Savings Accounts

College savings accounts are tax-advantaged college savings plans designed to help parents save money and finance higher education. The cost of a higher education can be quite high. *The Chronicle of Higher Education* has put together a table showing tuition and fees (1998–1999 through 2017–2018) for more than 3,000 colleges and institutions at https://www.chronicle.com/interactives/tuition-and-fees.

There are two main types of college savings accounts: 529 plans and Education Savings Accounts (also known as ESAs or Coverdell accounts). Both types of accounts allow you as the account owner to set up investment accounts for a beneficiary or recipient that you designate while offering tax-deferred growth. All contributions must be in cash. There are differences in how they can be used, contribution limits, income restrictions, account continuation, passing of control from parent to child, ability to change beneficiary, and who is qualified to open them.

If you've started a college savings plan, please enter the information in **Table 31**. This information can be found in your original account summary and in your statements. If you have more than one college savings account, use the second column.

Table 31: College Savings Accounts

Type: 529 or Coverdell		
Institution/state		
Owner (titling)		
Beneficiary		

Type of investment(s)		
Account number		
Number of shares, if applicable		
Date account established		
Cost basis per share/total		
As of date		
Current balance*		
Fees and expenses		
Details on any regularly scheduled contributions (amount, how often & how funded)*		
Location of documents*		
Website and log-in credentials		
Notes:		

*NEXT STEPS

From the table above, add any regular contributions as an expense on your cash flow statement (page 193). If you have a current ownership interest, enter the current balance on your net worth statement (page 199). Your original documents should be stored with your secure documents; add a recent statement to the assets section of your GET READY! binder.

Note

Proceeds from college savings accounts must be used to finance qualified education expenses, such as tuition, books, supplies, computers, and room and board. (There is some gray area on this, so be sure to check what is currently a qualified education expense.) Distributions, including any gains and investment income, can be withdrawn tax-free. Both plans are considered to be your assets, not your child's, which means their impact on financial aid is significantly reduced. However, any funds used for purposes other than qualified education expenses will be subject to a federal tax penalty of 10 percent on any earnings when funds are withdrawn. Many states also assess an additional 10 percent penalty. Be sure to also include any accounts started for your child by a third party, such as a grandparent, so you can use them in calculating the amount needed.

ABLE Accounts

An Achieving a Better Life Experience (ABLE) account is a type of tax-advantaged account that an eligible individual can use to save funds for the disability-related expenses of the account's designated beneficiary, who must be blind or disabled by a condition that began before the individual's 26th birthday. The accounts can be continued past age 26. An ABLE program can be established and maintained by a state or a state agency directly or by contracting with a private company (an instrument of the state). An eligible individual can be the designated beneficiary of only one ABLE account, which must be administered by a qualified ABLE program.

Tip

The ABLE National Resource Center provides a tool (ablenrc.org/state_compare) to search states and compare plans. There are some states that do not offer ABLE accounts. As with 529 plans, you can open an ABLE account with another state as the ABLE accounts do have varying fees, investment choices, and state tax rules.

Enter the information on any ABLE plans you contribute to in **Table 32**. This information can be found in your original account summary and in your statements. If you have more than one ABLE account, use the second column.

Table 32: ABLE Accounts

Institution/state (for account)		
Name of account holder (ownership titling)		
Beneficiary		
Account number		
Date account established		
Number of shares, if applicable		
Date purchased		
Cost basis per share/total		
As of date		
Current balance		
Fees and expenses		

Details on any regularly scheduled contributions (amount, how often & how funded)*		
Location of documents*		
Website and log-in credentials		
Notes:		

*NEXT STEPS

From the table above, add any regular contributions in the expense section of your cash flow statement (page 193). If you have a current ownership interest, enter the current balance on your net worth statement (page 199). Your original documents should be stored with your secure documents; add a recent statement to the assets section of your GET READY! binder.

END-OF-CHAPTER CHECK-IN

Did this chapter help you GET READY!? In the following table, assess your level of financial preparedness by checking the appropriate status box for all the topics in this chapter.

	In Progress	Completed	Not Applicable
Checking and savings accounts			
Certificate(s) of deposit (CD)			
Stocks			
Bonds			
Treasury securities (bills & bonds)			
Corporate bonds, government agency bonds, and municipal bonds			
Mutual funds			
Exchange-traded funds			
Collectibles			

Continued on next page . . .

	In Progress	Completed	Not Applicable
Stock options			
Business interests/ownerships			
Royalties			
Debts and obligations			
College savings accounts			
ABLE accounts			

 PRINT FORMS

To print these forms, visit my website at www.tonysteuer.com/resources.

NOTES

CHAPTER 4

Organizing Your Retirement Plan

The will to succeed is important, but what's more important is the will to prepare.
—Bobby Knight

Like I said when we started this journey together, the best first aid kit is the one that you have with you. If you forget to pack something, it's not there for you to use. Planning a first aid kit for an outdoor trip, for example, requires thought as to what type of first aid issues will arise on the trip. For example, if you are doing a 10-day backpacking trip, there are going to be a lot of blisters and other foot issues, so you'll need to pack more supplies than usual to treat foot injuries.

Retirement planning works the same way: You need to have the right supplies in your financial first aid kit to properly prepare for retirement. A comfortable retirement depends on your ability to be properly prepared and to use all of the financial tools available to you. And you'll want to keep track of all of your options. On the pages that follow, you'll be able to review the different types of plans available and enter the corresponding information on the type of plan you have.

Retirement accounts, with the exception of Roth IRAs, allow you to make contributions on a tax-free basis up to a certain amount. Withdrawals are subject to income tax (except with Roth IRAs). If you withdraw your money before age 59 ½, you could be subject to a 10 percent penalty! The exceptions to this rule are complex, so be sure to read the fine print before withdrawing from these accounts.

 GET READY!: ORGANIZING YOUR RETIREMENT PLAN ASSETS

In this chapter, we're going to take a look at your retirement plan assets. While organizing this part of the planner, you will learn about—

1. **Individual retirement accounts**. You will be making a list of all of your IRAs and Roth IRAs. You'll also record information about the accounts themselves, along with the balances.

2. **Self-employed and small business retirement accounts.** You'll make an inventory of any retirement account through a small business, such as a KEOGH, SEP-IRA, SARSEP IRA, Simple IRA, "solo" 401(k), and a defined-benefit plan.

3. **401(k), 403(b), and 457 plans.** Here you will document the value of any of these common retirement plans you would have through an employer.

4. **Pension plans.** I'll also ask you to gather information on any pension plans that you participate in.

5. **Other employer retirement programs.** You'll be able to add details of non-traditional retirement plans through a current or past employer, such as 409(a) non-qualified deferred compensation insurance plans, employee stock ownership plans (ESOPs), money purchase plans, and profit-sharing plans.

6. **Social Security.** You'll be able to take information from your annual Social Security statement and include it in your retirement assets. There are also instructions on how to request your Social Security statement.

Retirement planning is centered on the word "planning." Being able to comfortably retire is all about how you prepare for this major life event. In Chapter 10, you will be able to review a retirement timeline to help you calculate your projected retirement savings.

Individual Retirement Accounts (IRAs)

IRAs are investment accounts that allow you to save money for retirement. Once you've made your contribution to an IRA, you can invest in stocks, bonds, mutual funds, exchange-traded funds, and more. Keep in mind that some IRAs do have restrictions on certain investments, such as real estate, so do your homework before opening an IRA. You can set it up so that a specific amount is automatically deducted from your checking or savings account and deposited in the IRA.

Note

When you open an IRA, you have two options: a traditional IRA or a Roth IRA. The tax treatment of your contributions and withdrawals will depend on which option you select. Also, the after-tax value of your withdrawal will depend on the tax rate at the time of withdrawal and the type of IRA you choose.

1. **Traditional IRA:** Allows you to take a tax-deduction on contributions up to a specific amount each year. Interest accumulates on a tax-deferred basis. Income taxes are due on distribution (when you take money out).

2. **Roth IRA:** Allows you to make a non-deductible contribution up to a specific amount each year. Interest accumulates on a tax-deferred basis. Distributions are not subject to income tax.

In **Table 33**, you can add general information about your IRA account(s). Please note the total value of the IRA and where the IRA is held. Fill out the columns as applicable. If you have more than one account, use the second column.

Table 33: Individual Retirement Accounts

Type (Traditional IRA or Roth IRA)		
Account titling		
Financial institution/company holding IRA		
Account number		
Date account established		
As of date		
Current balance*		
Contributions (planned/frequency)*		
Beneficiary (primary and secondary) Location of beneficiary designation and other important information, such as the last time the beneficiary was updated		
Advisor name and contact info (if applicable)		
Location of documents		
Website and log-in credentials		
Notes:		

*NEXT STEPS

From the table above, add any regular contributions as an expense on your cash flow statement (page 193) and to the retirement calculation worksheet (page 204). Add the current account balance in the asset section of your net worth statement (page 199) and to the retirement calculator (page 204). Your original documents should be stored with your secure documents; add a recent statement to the assets section of your GET READY! binder.

Tip

Be sure to check on contribution limits, income eligibility, tax deductibility, and early-withdrawal penalties on the IRS website (www.irs.gov). It is important to ensure you satisfy the contribution eligibility requirements to avoid any IRS-assessed penalties.

Note

If you make a contribution to your IRA between January 1 and April 15, you will need to let your financial institution know the year to which the contribution must be applied. Writing the tax year in the memo field of your check should be sufficient. Failure to provide this information could result in the amount being applied to the wrong tax year.

Self-Employed and Small Business Individual Retirement Accounts

There are many options for those who are self-employed or employed in small businesses. Some of these options include a KEOGH, SEP-IRA, SARSEP IRA, Simple IRA, "solo" 401(k), and a defined-benefit plan. If you participate in a 401(k) through an employer, you still may be able to contribute to a separate plan if you are a sole proprietorship. The following list briefly describes each type of account.

Note

The following are the types of plans available to those who are self-employed or have small businesses.

- **KEOGH**: A program by which self-employed individuals may make tax-deferred contributions to a retirement plan.
- **SEP-IRA** (Simplified Employee Pension plan): A qualified plan that accepts employee and employer contributions to an employee's IRA.
- **SARSEP IRA**: This type of Simplified Employee Pension (SEP) plan needs to have been established before 1997.
- **Simple IRA** (Savings Incentive Match Plan for Employees): This plan allows employees and employers to contribute to traditional IRAs set up for employees. It is ideally suited as a start-up retirement savings plan for small employers not currently sponsoring a retirement plan.
- **Solo 401(k):** A 401(k) qualified retirement plan for Americans that was designed specifically for employers with no full-time employees other than the business owner and his or her spouse.
- **Defined-benefit plan:** A plan where contributions are calculated based on the benefit that you would receive at retirement based on your current age and expected investment returns.

In **Table 34**, add information on any of the above plans offered through your business that you participate in. You can find this information in the original plan summary, on a recent statement, or online. If you have more than one plan, use the second column.

Table 34: Self-Employed and Small Business Individual Retirement Accounts

Type: KEOGH, SEP-IRA, SARSEP IRA, Simple IRA, "solo" 401(k)		
Account titling		
Financial institution/company holding IRA		
Account number		
Date account established		
As of date		
Current account balance*		
Employer contribution		
Are employee contributions allowed?		
Contributions (planned/frequency)*		
Contribution limits		
Beneficiary (primary and secondary) Location of beneficiary designation and other important information, such as the last time the beneficiary was updated		
Advisor name and contact info (if applicable)		
Location of documents*		
Website and log-in credentials		
Notes:		

*NEXT STEPS

From the table above, add any regular contributions as an expense to your cash flow statement (page 193) and to the retirement calculation worksheet (page 204). Add any distributions to the income section of your cash flow statement (page 193). Add the current account balance to the asset section of your net worth statement (page 199) and to the retirement calculator (page 204). Your original documents should be stored with your secure documents; add a recent statement to the assets section of your GET READY! binder.

Employer Retirement Accounts

Some employers, especially larger employers, offer pension plans, qualified profit-sharing plans, and other forms of tax-deferred compensation for their employees. But these days it's more common for employers to offer retirements plans such as a 401(k) or 403(b). In fact, in 2016, 401(k) plans were offered by 81 percent of US employers.

401(k), 403(b), and 457 Plans

If you are offered a retirement plan such as a 401(k), 403(b) (also known as tax-sheltered annuities, or TSAs), or 457, you should sign up immediately. 403(b) plans are similar to 401(k) plans but are generally offered by government entities (such as public schools) and nonprofit organizations. Employers usually make a fixed contribution and sometimes offer an additional matching contribution. 401(k) and 403(b) plans usually offer a variety of investment options to choose from (usually mutual funds). It's important to monitor the expenses and fees, as some plans can have high administrative and investment expenses. If the investment expenses are higher than the expenses you'd incur if you invested in your own IRA, then you may want to contribute only what's necessary to get your employer match, and invest the rest in your own IRA. But keep in mind that fees on IRAs can be high as well.

Tip

Don't miss out on your employer's "match" to your 401(k) or 403(b). This is essentially free money, which many people fail to collect. This matching contribution can be a set dollar amount or a percentage of the employee's contribution. There are usually caps on employer matches, and there is a cap on how much you can contribute annually. One of the most common matches is a dollar-for-dollar match up to 3 percent of the employee's salary. Taking full advantage of the employer match doubles your savings. For example, if you set aside $48,000 in your 401(k) or 403(b) over the course of 20 years, by the time you retire, you will end up with double that—$84,000—because of your employer's contribution. That's $48,000 in free contributions! And it doesn't even include all the tax-deferred growth over those 20 years. So take advantage of employer matching whenever you can. This contribution is an immediate positive return on your contribution (investment).

Tip

Some employers will automatically enroll you in their 401(k) plan to a target date fund (based on when you are likely to retire) and a 3 percent contribution rate. Be sure to review the fund you are enrolled in, as you might prefer a lower-cost fund option such as an index fund. Consider, too, whether you should increase your contribution rate to meet your retirement goals. Most people will need to contribute more than 3 percent of their income.

If you participate or have participated in a 401(k), 403(b), or 457 plan through a current or past employer, fill out **Table 35** with any active plans you may have. You can find the information in your plan summary, benefit statements, or online. If you have more than one plan, use the second column.

Table 35: 401(k), 403(b), and 457 Plans

Type: 401(k), 403(b)/TSA, 457		
Employer		
Account titling		
Financial institution		
Account number		
Date of initial participation		
As of date		
Current total account value		
Current total vested account value*		
Employer match percentage		
Employer contribution (annual)		
Your contribution amount and frequency*		
Vesting status (for employer contributions; there is no vesting for employee contributions)		
Date fully vested*		
Loan balance (if any) and repayment details		
Loan interest rate		
Beneficiary (primary and secondary) Location of beneficiary designation and other important information, such as the last time the beneficiary was updated		
Employee benefits coordinator (or advisor)—name and contact information		
Location of documents		
Website and log-in credentials		
Notes:		

Continued on next page . . . ➡

Tip

401(k)s have historically had additional fees over and above the ordinary expenses (identified as "expense ratios") incurred by all mutual funds. These fees vary based on the plan that your employer has set up. These fees include marketing and distribution fees (12b-1 fees), sub-transfer agent fees, trading or transaction costs, wrap fees, trustee fees, legal fees, and audit fees. Total fees can exceed 2 percent per year, so be sure to allocate your funds into the lowest-expense options, or consider these fees if you have the opportunity to roll over your balance.

Tip

It is rare for most people to stay with the same employer, which means that you are likely to have multiple 401(k)s over the course of your work life and be faced with the decision of what to do with older 401(k)s. It's important to review the options of whether you can or should continue the 401(k) with your former employer, whether your former employer could require you to roll it over to an IRA, and if your current employer's 401(k) or 403(b) plan has lower fees than an IRA.

Pension Plans

Pension plans are a great benefit and unfortunately have become rare, so if your employer has a pension plan, it is important to get the details to ensure that you get the maximum benefit. Request or access an annual benefit statement. Details such as vesting period are important. This is the amount of time that you must be with an employer to receive the full benefit; usually plans will have a vesting schedule that offers a higher percentage the longer you are with them. Be sure to also consider what will happen to your pension benefit if you leave your employer.

On the facing page, add the details on any pension plans that you may have to **Table 36**. You can find this information in your employee handbook, statements (if you receive one), or online. If you have more than one plan, use the second column.

Table 36: Pension Plans

Employer/source		
Participant ID (or other identifier)		
Date enrolled in plan		
Date of eligibility for retirement		
As of date		
Current lump sum value*		
Estimated payout		
Restrictions/limitations		
Total accrued annual benefit		
Vesting status		
Date of being fully vested*		
Loan balance (if any) and repayment details		
Loan interest rate		
Estimated monthly benefit to be paid, monthly benefit (and lump sum amount)		
Survivor benefits (if applicable)		
Beneficiary		
HR contact/plan administrator (name and contact information)		
Location of documents		
Website and log-in credentials		
Notes:		

---

*NEXT STEPS ——————

From the table above, add the current lump sum account balance in the asset section of your net worth statement (page 199) and to the retirement calculator (page 204). Add date fully vested to your financial calendar (page 216). Your original documents should be stored with your secure documents; add a recent statement to the assets section of your GET READY! binder.

Note

When you go to take money from your pension plan, you will be faced with a big decision: whether to take your money in a lump sum or in a monthly payment (either just for your lifetime or other options to include a survivor benefit). Choose wisely, because once this choice is made, it cannot be undone. To learn more about this trade-off, visit http://files.consumerfinance.gov/f/201601_cfpb_pension -lump-sum-payouts-and-your-retirement-security.pdf.

Tip

Find out if there's an unclaimed pension: Over 38 million people in the US haven't claimed pension benefits they have earned. Find out if you, or someone you know, is owed a pension on the Pension Benefit Guaranty Corporation website: https://www.pbgc.gov/search/unclaimed-pensions.

Tip

Check the abandoned plan database maintained by the US Department of Labor to track down the current trustee of your cash. If the retirement benefits were through a traditional pension plan for a company that no longer exists, try the unclaimed pensions database of the US Pension Benefit Guaranty Corporation (https://www.askebsa.dol.gov/AbandonedPlanSearch).

Other Employer and Group Retirement Plans

There are other less common plans that can be provided through an employer. It is important to list details about these plans and to include them in your overall planning. Below are some of the less common plans:

- **409A non-qualified deferred compensation plans:** Section 409A applies to compensation that workers earn in one year but that is paid in a future year. This is referred to as non-qualified deferred compensation. This is different from deferred compensation in the form of elective deferrals to qualified plans (such as a 401(k) plan) or to a 403(b) or 457(b) plan.

- **Employee stock ownership plan (ESOP):** This is an employee-owner program that provides a company's workforce with an ownership interest in the company. In an ESOP, companies provide their employees with stock ownership, often at no upfront cost to the employees. ESOP shares, however, are part of employees' remuneration for work performed. Shares are allocated to employees and may be held in an ESOP trust until the employee retires or leaves the company. The shares are then either bought back by the company for redistribution or voided.

- **Money purchase plan:** Money purchase plans have required contributions. The employer is required to make a contribution to the plan each year for the plan participants. With a money purchase plan, the plan states the contribution percentage that is required. If the plan has a contribution of 5 percent of each eligible employee's pay, your employer will need to make a contribution of 5 percent of each eligible employee's pay to their separate account. A participant's benefit is based on the amount of contributions to their account and the gains or losses associated with the account at the time of retirement.

- **Profit-sharing plan:** Any plan in which a portion of the profits of a company are set aside for distribution to its employees. The employer can decide the specific dollar amount they will contribute. Then, depending on the plan's contribution formula, that amount is allocated to the separate accounts of the eligible employees.

In **Table 37**, add the details on any other employer or group retirement plans that you may have. You can find this information in your employee handbook, plan description statements (if you receive one), or online. If you have more than one plan, use the second column.

Table 37: Other Employer and Group Retirement Plans

Type of plan		
Employer or group (if applicable)		
Account number or other identifier		
Date first participating in plan		
As of date		
Who contributes (employer, employee, or both)		
Employer contribution amount or percentage		
Employee contribution amount or percentage and frequency*		
Contribution limits		
Vesting requirements		
Current vested balance		
Plan administrator name and contact info		
Location of documents		
Website and log-in credentials		
Notes:		

Continued on next page . . . ➡

Social Security

Social Security is a federal government program that provides a source of income for you or your legal dependents (spouse, children, or parents) if you qualify for benefits. You also need a Social Security number to get a job. While you work, you pay Social Security taxes. This tax money goes into a trust fund that pays benefits to those who are currently retired, to people with disabilities, and to the surviving spouses and children of workers who have died. Each year you work, you'll get credits to help you become eligible for benefits when it's time for you to retire.

Note

Social Security benefits are *not intended to be your only source of income when you retire.* On average, Social Security will replace about 40 percent of your annual pre-retirement earnings. You will need other savings, investments, pensions, or retirement accounts to make sure you have enough money to live comfortably when you retire.

Note

To complete the table below, you'll need to order your Social Security statement. This statement indicates how much you or your family would receive in disability, survivor, or retirement benefits. It also includes a record of your lifetime earnings. It's important to review this statement for accuracy as your benefits are based on the record of lifetime earnings.

To order your Social Security statement, you'll need to establish an account on the official Social Security website: www.ssa.gov. Once you've established an account, you can download your statement. It's important to do this periodically, as noted on the financial calendar on page 216.

Once you have your Social Security statement, enter the information from your statement in **Table 38**.

Table 38: Social Security

Name on Social Security card	
Social Security number (keep this secure)	
Date eligible for full Social Security benefit	
Age at which you plan to take Social Security	
As of date	
Estimated annual Social Security benefit*	
If you are eligible to receive a Social Security benefit based on someone else's earnings, add in the name of the person and the reason—widow, divorced spouse, spouse earning higher income	
Is your earnings record correct? (If not, notify the Social Security Administration.)	
Location of documents	
Website log-in credentials	
Notes:	

*NEXT STEPS

From the table above, add the estimated annual benefit to your retirement tracker (step 3) (page 204). Your original documents should be stored with your secure documents; add a recent statement to the assets section of your GET READY! binder.

Tip

Choosing when to take Social Security payments is an important decision, with numerous pros and cons. You can elect to take Social Security before your full retirement age; however, you will receive a lower monthly benefit. The longer you wait to take Social Security, the higher the monthly benefit will be. Your retirement age depends on the year you were born and is shown on your Social Security statement. You can also use a Social Security online calculator (http://www.consumerfinance.gov /retirement/before-you-claim) to determine the optimal age to claim your Social Security benefits.

Tip

For a new Social Security card or a replacement card, call your local Social Security Administration (SSA) office for assistance at (800) 772-1213, visit your local office, or go online at www.ssa.gov.

 END-OF-CHAPTER CHECK-IN

Did this chapter help you GET READY!? In the following table, assess your level of financial preparedness by checking the appropriate status box for all the topics in this chapter.

	In Progress	Completed	Not Applicable
Individual retirement accounts			
Self-employed and small business retirement accounts			
401(k), 403(b) and 457 plans			
Pension plans			
Other employer retirement plans			
Social Security			

 PRINT FORMS

To print these forms, visit my website at www.tonysteuer.com/resources.

NOTES

_____

_____

_____

_____

_____

_____

_____

CHAPTER 5

Listing Your Home and Real Estate/Real Property

Preparedness, when properly pursued, is a way of life, not a sudden spectacular program.
—SPENCER W. KIMBALL

When responding to an emergency that will require a rescue or medical care, the first rule is to survey the scene. It's important to gather all of the information, to remain calm, and above all else, to not become another person who needs help. Becoming an additional person who needs help increases the number of resources necessary to make an effective rescue or to give proper treatment.

Like a medical situation, you can also survey your property "scene" by documenting all of your property. You will want to ensure it is properly protected through insurance and to have the details necessary for repairs or replacement should there be any issues. This helps you move forward to being part of your property "rescue team" instead of just being a bystander. Organizing this information and noting the details will also help your heirs if something should happen to you and minimize the resources needed to provide financial first aid.

Property ownership, whether it's a home, an auto, a boat, or your home furnishings, represents a large portion of your overall financial life and should be monitored appropriately.

 GET READY!: ORGANIZING YOUR PROPERTY

In this chapter, we're going to take a look at your assets that fall under the category of personal property. While organizing this part of the planner, you will learn about—

1. **Home (primary residence).** You will be listing details regarding your home ownership and valuation.

2. **Vacation homes, second homes, and time-shares.** You'll make an inventory of all the property you own for personal use along with relevant details.

3. **Investment property.** You also will be documenting the value of any property that is used strictly for investment purposes, such as rentals or property to be improved and re-sold.

4. **Farmland.** You'll gather information on any farmland that you own.

5. **Commercial property.** This is property used for business activities. Commercial property is treated differently for legal, tax, and insurance purposes than investment property.

6. **Cars.** Here's where you can include information about your cars, covering everything from make and model to registration.

7. **Personal property inventory.** You can list all of your major personal items such as appliances, computers, and entertainment systems.

Property is a complex investment that needs to be carefully managed and protected. In this chapter, we'll focus on property ownership and values. In later chapters, you'll enter related information such as loans, taxes, insurance, and utilities.

Home (Primary Residence)

Owning a home is more than just buying a house or condominium. It is a financial asset, and the impact on your financial life needs to be taken into account. Understanding all of the various aspects of managing your home is like running a mini-business. You have to make sure that all of the bills are paid and that everything is in working order.

In **Table 39**, enter information regarding your home, including current value, improvements, and major repairs.

Table 39: Home (Primary Residence)

Residence/property location (full address)	
Date purchased (closing date)	
Type of ownership (sole, community property, joint with right of survivorship, tenant in common, in trust, life estate)	
Name of any co-owner and percentage you own	
Purchase price	

Current estimated value (comparable property—see Zillow.com or Trulia.com)*	
As of date	
Alarm location, code, and secret phrase	
Homeowners association (name, account #, and contact information)	
Home improvements and repairs (description, permit info, date of improvement, cost of improvement, document location)	
Location of documents (including real estate deed)	
Notes (include any easements):	

*NEXT STEPS

From the table above, enter the current value of your home in the asset section of your net worth statement (page 199). Keep your deed, original purchase documents, permits, and documentation for major home improvements and repairs with your secure documents. Add copies of these documents to the real estate/property section of your GET READY! binder.

Tip

It is important to document any home improvements and repairs, as they will increase the value of your home. When you sell the property, these receipts will save you significant money by increasing the cost basis of the property and thus reducing your taxable income.

Tip

You can receive financial help from the US government to repair and improve your home. Eligibility requirements vary from program to program. In general, it depends on your income level, age, type of property, and where the property is located. To apply, you'll need to reach out to the federal, state, or county government agency that administers the program. Loans are made by traditional lenders; however, the government programs help these lenders make loans that they might normally not fulfill. Grants are available depending on your income level and work to be done.

Vacation Home/Secondary Residence

A second home is a residence that you intend to occupy for part of the year in addition to your primary home. Second homes are typically used as vacation homes. Sometimes they are used more frequently than simply for vacations, such as for a season or a regularly visited business location.

In **Table 40**, enter details on any vacation home or secondary residence that you own.

Table 40: Vacation Home/Secondary Residence

Property location (full address)	
Date purchased (closing date)	
Type of ownership (sole, community property, joint with right of survivorship, tenant in common, in trust, life estate)	
Name of any co-owner and percentage you own	
Purchase price	
Current estimated value (comparable property—see Zillow.com or Trulia.com)*	
As of date	
Alarm location, code, and secret phrase	
Homeowners association (name, account #, and contact information)	
Property management company (name, contact information, and purpose)	
Improvements and repairs (description, permit info, date of improvement, cost of improvement, document location)	
Location of documents (including real estate deed)	
Notes (include any easements):	

*NEXT STEPS

From the table above, enter the current value of your vacation home or secondary residence in the asset section of your net worth statement (page 199). Keep your deed, original purchase documents, permits, and documentation for major property improvements and repairs with your secure documents. Add copies of these documents to the real estate/property section of your GET READY! binder.

Time-Share/Vacation Club

A time-share (sometimes called vacation ownership) is a property with a divided form of ownership or use rights. These properties are typically resort condominium units in which multiple parties hold rights to use the property, and each owner of the same accommodation is allotted a period of time to use the property. The minimum purchase is a one-week ownership, with the high-season weeks demanding higher prices. Units may be sold as a partial ownership, lease, or "right to use," in which case the latter holds no claim to ownership of the property. The ownership of time-share programs is varied and has been changing for decades.

In **Table 41**, enter details on any time-share or vacation club you belong to.

Table 41: Time-Share/Vacation Club

Property location (full address)	
Time-share/vacation club full name and contact information	
Account number or member ID	
Type of ownership (sole, community property, joint with right of survivorship, tenant in common, in trust, life estate)	
Name of any co-owner and percentage you own	
Date purchased (closing date)	
Purchase price	
Contract/membership expiration date*	
Annual points allotment	
Contract/use-year expiration month*	
Point banking deadline (if applicable)*	
Beneficiary (if applicable)	
Location of documents	
Website and log-in credentials	
Notes (easements, other things of note):	

*NEXT STEPS

From the table above, enter the contract use-year expiration date, points banking deadline date, and contract expiration date on your financial calendar (page 216). Keep your documents with your secure documents. Add a recent statement (if available) to the real estate/property section of your GET READY! binder.

Note

The majority of time-shares and vacation clubs usually have no value, so there is no need to enter them on your net worth statement (page 199). You may be able to pass on your interest to your heirs, so it is important to include your membership in your estate planning.

There are time-share redemption companies. However, the time-share resale market is oversaturated, and you may see some time-shares listed on eBay for as little as $1. Time-share redemption companies can help you negotiate with time-share wholesalers or transfer your time-share back to the travel club, resort, or an inventory aggregate by means of exclusive partnerships and deals.

There are a few popular time-share clubs, like the Disney Vacation Club, where you may be able to transfer your contract back to them. There are also many scams in the time-share resale market. Be sure to research your options before entering into any agreements.

Investment Property

Investment property is purchased in order to generate income, profit from appreciation, or take advantage of certain tax benefits. This is property that is not used as a primary or secondary home. It can be a rental property (residential or commercial) or property purchased for the purpose of "flipping" it (buying a house at a low price, remodeling or renovating it, and selling it at a higher price).

In **Table 42**, enter details on any investment property you own.

Table 42: Investment Property

Property location (full address)	
Date purchased (closing date)	
Type of ownership (sole, community property, joint with right of survivorship, tenant in common, in trust, life estate)	
Name of any co-owner and percentage you own	
Purchase price	
Current estimated value (comparable property— see Zillow.com or Trulia.com)*	
As of date	
Purpose of investment (rental, flipping, other)	
Alarm location, code, and secret phrase	
Property improvements and repairs (description, permit info, date of improvement, cost of improvement, document location)	
Homeowners association (name, account #, and contact information)	
Renter's name and phone number (if applicable)	

Property management company name, contact person, and information	
Rental agreement (if applicable)	
Rental agreement terms (how long, monthly rent and method of payment, security deposit)*	
Location of documents (including real estate deed)	
Notes (include any easements and plans for the property):	

*NEXT STEPS

From the table above, enter the current value of your property in the asset section of your net worth statement (page 199). If there are any important dates relevant to the property, such as rental agreement expiration, add them to your financial calendar (page 216). Keep your deed, original purchase documents, permits, and documentation for major property improvements and repairs with your secure documents. Add copies of these documents to the real estate/property section of your GET READY! binder.

Farmland

Farmland is used for agricultural purposes. Specific tax laws and rules apply to farmland, and as such, it is managed differently from other property. In **Table 43**, enter details on any farmland that you own.

Table 43: Farmland

Property location (full address)	
Date purchased (closing date)	
Type of ownership (sole, community property, joint with right of survivorship, tenant in common, in trust, life estate)	
Name of any co-owner and percentage you own	
Purchase price	
Current estimated value (comparable property)*	
As of date	
Alarm location, code, and secret phrase	
Purpose—main function (dairy, crops, or other)	
Location of documents (including real estate deed)	
Notes (easements, plans for the property):	

Continued on next page . . . ➡

Undeveloped Land

Undeveloped land can be held for investment purposes and/or is sometimes inherited. Oftentimes there is no plan for it, while in other cases, there may be concrete plans in place, including an impending sale or development. In **Table 44** below, enter details on any undeveloped land that you own.

Table 44: Undeveloped Land

Property location (full address or other identifying information)	
Date purchased (closing date)	
Type of ownership (sole, community property, joint with right of survivorship, tenant in common, in trust, life estate)	
Name of any co-owner and percentage you own	
Purchase price	
Current estimated value (comparable property)*	
As of date	
Alarm location, code, and secret phrase	
Plans for the property, including where details of these plans can be found	
Property improvements and repairs (description, permit info, date of improvement, cost of improvement, document location)	
Location of documents (including real estate deed)	
Notes (easements):	

secure documents. Add copies of these documents to the real estate/property section of your GET READY! binder.

Commercial Property

Commercial property refers to real estate property that is used for business activities. Commercial property usually refers to buildings that house businesses; however, it can also refer to land that is intended to generate a profit, as well as larger residential rental properties. The designation of a property as a commercial property has implications on the financing of the building, the tax treatment, and the laws that apply to it. Commercial property includes malls, grocery stores, office buildings, manufacturing shops, and much more.

In **Table 45**, enter details on any commercial property that you own. If you have a larger commercial real estate portfolio, indicate the total values, location of documents, and details.

Table 45: Commercial Property

Residence/property location (full address)	
Date purchased (closing date)	
Type of ownership (sole, community property, joint with right of survivorship, tenant in common, in trust, life estate)	
Name of any co-owner and percentage you own	
Purchase price	
Current estimated value (comparable property)*	
As of date	
Alarm location, code, and secret phrase	
Management company (name, account #, and contact information)	
Property improvements and repairs (description, permit info, date of improvement, cost of improvement, document location)	
Location of documents (including real estate deed)	
Notes (easements):	

> ***NEXT STEPS**
>
> From the table above, enter the current value of your commercial property in the asset section of your net worth statement (page 199). Keep your deed, original purchase documents, permits, and documentation for major improvements and repairs with your secure documents. Add copies of these documents and/or a summary of your commercial real estate portfolio to the real estate/property section of your GET READY! binder.

Cars

The average American household owns an estimated two cars each, so that's a whole lot of cars. The costs affiliated with cars are an important consideration in our financial lives.

Note

It's important to consider all the costs when buying a car and doing what makes sense for you in terms of your budget and investment/retirement goals. Is the trade-off of having a nice car with all of the extras, along with extended warranties and anti-theft devices and other add-ons, worth the financial impact? Knowing your true bottom line will help you make a sound decision.

In **Table 46**, add details about your car(s). If you own more than two cars, you can add information in the Notes section at the end of this chapter.

Table 46: Cars

	Car 1	Car 2
Make		
Model		
Year		
Vehicle identification number (VIN)		
Date purchased or leased		
Type of ownership or lease (sole, community property, joint with right of survivorship, tenant in common, in trust, life estate)		
Name of any co-owner and percentage you own		
License plate		
Primary driver (full name)		
State of registration		
Registration expiration date*		
Amount paid		
Current value (find a car's current value online at www.edmunds.com or www.kbb.com, Kelley Blue Book)*		
As of date		
Location of keys		

	Car 1	Car 2
Alarm code and details		
Name of regular repair shop (contact info)		
Warranty and/or extended warranty expiration date		
Title location		
Location of documents (title, maintenance records, recalls, repairs)		
Notes (recalls, major repairs):		

*NEXT STEPS

From the table above, enter the current value of your car(s) in the asset section of your net worth statement (page 199). Add the registration expiration and warranty expiration dates to your financial calendar (page 216). Keep your title, original purchase documents, permits, and documentation for major home improvements and repairs with your secure documents. Add copies of these documents to the real estate/property section of your GET READY! binder.

 Tip

It is advisable to wait until your car is near the end of the original warranty period before extending your current warranty. You can then compare the manufacturer extended warranty with other options. At that point, you'll have an idea of your average repair and maintenance costs to assess if extending the warranty is worthwhile.

Planes, Boats, and Recreational Vehicles

If you have a plane, boat, or recreational vehicle, you most likely have put a lot of time in to caring for and enjoying it. It is important to list details about this part of your life so that you have the information for an insurance claim and so these assets can be enjoyed by your heirs.

If you own a plane, boat, or recreational vehicle, enter the details in **Table 47**. If you own more than one, you can enter it in the Notes section at the end of this chapter.

Table 47: Planes, Boats, and Recreational Vehicles

Type (plane, boat, or RV)	
Make	
Model	
Year	
Date purchased	
Type of ownership (sole, community property, joint with right of survivorship, tenant in common, in trust, life estate)	
Name of any co-owner and percentage you own	
Vehicle identification number (VIN)	
Registration	
State of registration	
Registration expiration date	
Amount paid	
Current value*	
As of date	
Primary user's name	
License or certification (type, location, and expiration date)	
Keys—where they are kept	
Location of item (airfield, marina)	
Security—alarm code and info	
Name of regular mechanic/repair shop	
Warranty and/or extended warranty details and expiration*	
Improvements and repairs (description, permit info, date of improvement, cost of improvement, document location)	
Location of documents (title, maintenance records, recalls, repairs)*	
Notes (recalls):	

*NEXT STEPS

From the table above, enter the current value of your boat, plane, or RV in the asset section of your net worth statement (page 199). Add any registration, warranty, and storage expiration dates to your financial calendar (page 216). Keep your title, original purchase documents, permits, and documentation for major improvements and repairs with your secure documents. Add copies of these documents to the real estate/property section of your GET READY! binder.

Taking Inventory of Major Property

Throughout our lives, we purchase personal property. It's important to keep a record of our major personal property items in the event that you have to file an insurance claim in case of a burglary, fire, flood, earthquake, or other event.

Tip

As you enter the current values for your property, be careful not to overvalue items such as appliances, computer equipment, car phones, and home entertainment items; these may not be worth as much as you think. Estimate a price based on a reasonable fair market value. A review of the classified section of your local newspaper or www.ebay.com will provide a good start for determining these values.

In **Table 48**, add information about your main possessions and be sure to keep copies of receipts, purchase contracts, and appraisals. This information can usually be found on the item itself and sometimes on the original packaging or documentation.

Table 48: Taking Inventory of Major Property

	Brand/ Make	Model Number	Serial Number	Location (physical)	Estimated Value	Warranty (expiration date)	Notes and Documents Location/ Purchase Price and Date
BBQ grill							
Clothing							
Cell phone							
Computer/ laptop 1							

Continued on next page . . .

	Brand/ Make	Model Number	Serial Number	Location (physical)	Estimated Value	Warranty (expiration date)	Notes and Documents Location/ Purchase Price and Date
Computer/ laptop 2							
Dishwasher							
Washer							
Dryer							
Furniture (estimate)							
Stove (range)							
Oven							
Printer(s)							
Refrigerator							
Sporting equipment							
Stereos							
Tablet 1 (iPad, Kindle)							
Tablet 2							
Television 1							
Television 2							
Tools							
Video game system(s)							
Appliances (other)— estimate							
Other							
Notes:							

Note

I recommend that you also keep a detailed home inventory. There are many tools to help you do so, from spreadsheets to apps. A good app to use to take pictures and categorize this information is offered by the National Association of Insurance Commissioners and is called "Scr.app.book" (http://www.insureuonline.org/insureu_special_disaster.htm). You should also upload pictures to a storage website such as iCloud or Dropbox. An easy way to do this is to go room by room, noting these items.

END-OF-CHAPTER CHECK-IN

Did this chapter help you GET READY!? In the following table, assess your level of financial preparedness by checking the appropriate status box for all the topics in this chapter.

	In Progress	Completed	Not Applicable
Home (primary residence)			
Vacation home/secondary residence			
Time-share/vacation club			
Investment property			
Farmland			
Undeveloped land			
Commercial property			
Cars			
Planes, boats, and recreational vehicles			
Personal property inventory			

PRINT FORMS

To print these forms, visit my website at www.tonysteuer.com/resources.

✏️ NOTES

CHAPTER 6

Compiling Your Income (Earnings)

The secret of getting ahead is getting started.
—Mark Twain

Getting started in preparing for an emergency situation, as with anything, is to take the first step and then to keep going. A big part of being prepared is knowing what your resources are. If you are not familiar with your first aid supplies, then you may not have the right supplies handy when you need them.

Your income earnings, including that from work, investments, retirement plans, and other sources, are the resources that you have in your financial first aid kit. In this chapter, we'll review what those resources are so that you will be able to see the big picture. Having income, from whatever source, allows us to pay our bills and to enjoy our leisure time, so it is a crucial part of organizing your financial life.

 GET READY!: ORGANIZING YOUR INCOME

In this chapter, we're going to take a look at your income sources. Income is money that you have to support yourself and your loved ones. Being able to live comfortably can depend on your income and expenses. You'll be able to review expenses in Chapter 7 and review your cash flow statement in Chapter 10. While organizing this part of the planner, you will learn about—

1. **Compensation from your primary occupation.** In this part, you will be adding details that you get from your employment or primary business, whether you are an owner, partner, or sole proprietor. You'll also be able to include the "hidden value" of benefits received from your employer so you can have an overview of your total compensation.

2. **Other earned income.** You'll also add details about income from a second job, whether it's a traditional employee situation, participating in the gig economy (think: Uber or Lyft), or having your own business (side-hustle).

3. **Royalties.** You will be documenting any applicable income you receive from royalties such as copyrights, trademarks, and patents.

4. **Investment income.** I'll also ask you to gather information on any income you receive from investments such as CDs, stocks, and bonds.

5. **Retirement income.** If you are retired, you'll be able to add the details of any income received from Social Security, pensions, 401(k)s, IRAs, and other plans.

Create Your Total Compensation Statement

A major part of anyone's life is what they do to earn a living. While this may take the form of employment, business ownership, or freelancing, the bottom line is that all of us trade our time and skills for compensation. Here's where you write your own details. Having this written down will help you whether you are applying for a job, a loan, or some types of insurance.

When you work for a business as an owner, partner, or employee, you will typically receive compensation beyond your salary. You may receive additional cash in the form of bonuses or commissions. You will also probably receive employee benefits such as health insurance, life insurance, and disability insurance. And you may also be able to participate in retirement plans and possibly even receive stock incentives.

It's important to look at all of this as your total compensation package so that you can understand what your employer does (and does not do) for you and to ensure that you are maximizing your benefits. Your employer will withhold a portion of your earnings for federal and state income taxes (as applicable) along with Social Security and Medicare taxes. Your employer will also usually have you pay a share of some or all of your insurance benefits.

Table 49 will help you record basic information regarding your employment earnings. Depending on your company, you can find this information either through your company's online web portal or your annual open enrollment paperwork.

Table 49: Basic Employment Earnings Information

Employer or business name	
Business address and phone number	
Current position (title)	
Duties	
Date hired	
Number of dependents on W-4 statement	
Names of dependents listed on your W4 statement	

Date W-4 statement was last reviewed	
Benefits open enrollment period (dates)*	
Location of employment documents*	
Supervisor name and contact info	
HR website and log-in credentials (or contact name and phone number)	
Notes:	

*NEXT STEPS

From the table above, add your open enrollment period to your financial calendar (page 216).

Note

Open enrollment is a period of time each year when you can make changes to your benefits, including funding for retirement plans and flexible spending accounts. Be sure to review your options carefully to make sure your benefits still fit your needs and goals. Typically, there are also special enrollment periods, when you can make changes during a plan year if you have a major life event such as a marriage or birth of a child.

Tip

The IRS has a withholding calculator that will help you fill out your W-4 form and help you have the right amount of income tax withheld. You can access this calculator at https://www.irs.gov/individuals/irs-withholding-calculator.

Cash Compensation

As an employee, you receive cash compensation. The other part of your total compensation is the value of the benefits that you receive. The value of these benefits is your "hidden paycheck." The following tables provide a total compensation statement and will give you an overview of all of your compensation including cash compensation and employee benefits. It's important to take your total compensation into consideration when considering a new position or venture. Usually the longer you stay with an employer, the more you will see increases in salary and bonuses, along with more vacation days.

In **Table 50**, enter the various components of your annual compensation. You should receive a summary of your compensation from your employer with this information.

Table 50: Cash Compensation

Values as of date	
Salary (base pay)	$
Bonuses	$
Commissions	$
Other cash compensation (partnership, other distributions)	$
Benefit flex credit (from employer)	$
Total annual cash compensation*	$
Total daily compensation (divide annual compensation by 365)	$
Payment frequency	
Payment periods in a year	
Is payment through check or auto-deposit? For auto-deposit, indicate account to which pay is deposited	
Notes:	

*NEXT STEPS

From the table above, enter your annual compensation into the income section of your cash flow statement (page 193). Add a recent pay statement to the income section of your GET READY! binder.

Paid Time Off

Many employers are now combining vacation days and sick days to a total called "PTO" (paid time off days). PTO days may also be displayed on your pay stub, denoted as hours. These PTO days are oftentimes available to be "cashed out" at retirement or when you leave a company. If you've worked at a company a long time, you may have hundreds of PTO hours.

In **Table 51**, enter your PTO benefits for the calendar year beginning January 1. This information can be found on your annual open enrollment summary or your company's benefits website.

Table 51: Paid Time Off

Paid Leave	Accrual per Pay Period	Accrual per Year (multiply accrual per pay period by # of pay periods in a year)	Total Days Accrued
As of date			
Vacation days			
Accrued sick leave			
Paid holidays			
PTO days			
Other types of leave (such as extended sick leave, bereavement leave, jury duty leave, military leave, family leave, medical leave)			
Total paid days off (add all days off)			Not applicable
Cash value of annual paid time off (multiply accrual per year by compensation per day)	$ _____	$ _____	Not applicable
Notes:			

Group (Employee) Benefits and Deductions

In the table on the next page, you'll be adding a top-level summary of your employee benefits and the deductions for these group benefits. You'll enter details about your insurance in Chapter 8. For this table, enter the annual costs of your employee benefits premiums, retirement plan contribution, and other deductions from your pay. (Note: If information is only available on a per pay period basis, then multiply the pay-period amount times the number of pay periods in a year.)

You can find the information you need for **Table 52** in your open enrollment benefits confirmation or on your employee benefits website.

Table 52: Group (Employee) Benefits and Deductions

	Benefit Option (enter N/A if not elected)	Coverage Level	Annual Pre-Tax Deduction	Annual Post-Tax Deduction
EMPLOYEE BENEFITS (INSURANCE)				
Medical insurance			$	$
Dental insurance			$	$
Vision insurance			$	$
Basic life insurance			$	$
Basic accidental death & dismemberment (AD&D) insurance			$	$
Short-term disability insurance			$	$
Long-term disability insurance			$	$
Optional life insurance			$	$
Dependent life insurance			$	$
Optional AD&D			$	$
Other insurance benefits (such as long-term care)			$	$
Subtotal: Employee benefits paid by employer (A)			**$**	**$**

RETIREMENT PLAN CONTRIBUTIONS

	Benefit Option (enter N/A if not elected)	Coverage Level	Annual Pre-Tax Deduction	Annual Post-Tax Deduction
401(k)			$	$
Other retirement plan			$	$
Retirement plan total contributions (B)			**$**	**$**

SPENDING ACCOUNTS

	Benefit Option (enter N/A if not elected)	Coverage Level	Annual Pre-Tax Deduction	Annual Post-Tax Deduction
Flexible spending account			$	$
Dependent care spending account			$	$
Spending accounts subtotal (C)			**$**	**$**

	Benefit Option (enter N/A if not elected)	Coverage Level	Annual Pre-Tax Deduction	Annual Post-Tax Deduction
OTHER BENEFITS				
Employee assistance program			$_____	$_____
Transportation program*			$_____	$_____
Other (such as tuition reimbursement)			$_____	$_____
Subtotal of other benefits (D)			$_____	$_____
Subtotal benefit costs (Add A+B+C+D)			$_____	$_____
Total flex credit from employer			$_____	$_____
Total estimated pay deductions (benefit costs less flex credit)*			$_____	$_____
Location of benefits documents*				
Notes:				

---

*NEXT STEPS ────────────────────────────────────

Any 401(k) and other retirement plan contributions that you entered above should also be entered in your retirement savings worksheet (page 204). Include the total estimated pay deductions from the table above in the expenses section of your cash flow statement (page 193). Be sure to note the last date to use funds on your financial calendar (page 216). If you receive a summary of benefits annually, add it to the income section of your GET READY! binder.

Note

There are two types of spending accounts.

- **Flexible spending accounts**: You can make pre-tax contributions to a flexible spending account for out-of-pocket qualifying medical costs (deductibles, co-pays, eyeglasses, and more). This allows you to use pre-tax dollars to pay for after-tax costs. It's important to note that you can carry over only $500 of unused benefits for the following year, so anything over $500 will be forfeited.

- **Dependent care spending account:** This type of account allows you to make pre-tax contributions to a special account to pay for qualifying child care (and sometimes elder care) expenses. Currently any unused funds in your dependent care spending account cannot be rolled over to the following year, so you would forfeit the entire remaining balance.

Total Compensation

Compiling your total compensation will allow you to see the full value of your annual payment and other benefits from an employer or business. Your total compensation can dramatically increase what you take home in salary. To calculate your total compensation in **Table 53**, use the total values from the prior tables (**Table 50**: Cash Compensation, **Table 51**: Paid Time Off, and **Table 52**: Group (Employee) Benefits).

Table 53: Total Compensation

Cash compensation	$_____
Paid time off value	$_____
Company benefits contributions (or flex credit)	$_____
Total compensation (add figures above)	$_____

Dependents Coverage

In **Table 54**, list which of your dependents are covered through your employee benefit plan. This information can be found on your annual benefit summary or your employer's online benefits website.

Table 54: Dependents Coverage

Dependent Name	Medical Coverage (Y/N)	Dental Coverage (Y/N)	Dependent Life (Y/N)	Dependent AD&D (Y/N)

Other Earned Income: Second Job, Sharing (Gig) Economy, Side-Hustle

Many of us have income from sources other than our primary job. This can include a traditional second job or a non-traditional form of work, such as running a website, driving for Uber or Lyft, renting your home or rental property on Airbnb, or having an online store. It's important to add details about these other sources of income so you can keep track of them for yourself and so your heirs will receive any rightful income and be able to easily wrap up your affairs.

In **Table 55**, you can add information about income from a second job, whether it's an employee position, a contractor position, or as an owner (no employer). You can locate this income on any recent statement or the entity's online portal.

Table 55: Other Earned Income: Second Job, Sharing (Gig) Economy, Side-Hustle

Name of income source	
Relationship (employer, contractor, owner)	
Title (if applicable)	
Is this a business or hobby? (see note below)	
Annual net earned income*	
As of date	
How income is paid	
Account to which income is deposited	
Website and log-in credentials	
Location of documents	
Notes:	

*NEXT STEPS

Add the annual net earned income to your cash flow statement (page 193). Store any documents with your secure documents. Add a recent account statement to the income section of your GET READY! binder.

Note

It's important for tax purposes that you distinguish between whether a pursuit is a business or a hobby, as this will affect whether it has an impact on your financial life. If you are earning income, you will need to report it. If you want to be able to deduct expenses on your taxes, you'll need to make sure that it meets IRS qualifications for being a business. You can find a list of the IRS criteria at https://www.irs.gov/faqs/small-business-self-employed-other-business/income-expenses/income-expenses.

Online Income/Sales

Using an online store is a popular way to sell both new and used physical goods along with digital goods. In **Table 56**, you can add details if you are selling online, whether you have an online store or are just selling items on eBay.

Table 56: Online Income/Sales

Name of site (Amazon, eBay, Etsy, other)	
Business or hobby (see note above)	
Annual net earned income*	
As of date	
How income is paid (check or auto-deposit)	
Account to which income is deposited	
What's sold (or inventory list location)	
Inventory location	
Website and log-in credentials	
Document location*	
Notes:	

> ***NEXT STEPS**
>
> From the table above, enter the annual net earned income onto the income section of the cash flow statement (page 193). Store any original documents with your secure documents. Also, you will want to add your most recent annual statement to the income section of your GET READY! binder.

Royalties (Copyrights, Trademarks, Patents, and Other Property That Can Be Licensed)

Royalties are compensation paid to the owner of a right such as copyright, patent, franchise, trademark, or other licensed property. Royalty payments are made to the legal owner.

In **Table 57**, add all pertinent information about any royalty income you receive. You can find this information in any contracts or agreements and on statements you receive.

Table 57: Royalties (Copyrights, Trademarks, Patents, and Other Property That Can Be Licensed)

Name of property	
Name of entity/licensee who makes payment	
Annual distribution*	
As of date	
How income is paid	
Account to which income is deposited	
Beneficiary or survivor benefit? If yes, enter name	
Website and log-in credentials	
Location of documents*	
Notes:	

*NEXT STEPS

From the table above, enter your annual royalty distribution in the income section on your cash flow statement (page 193). Store agreements and other documents with your secure documents. Add a recent statement to the income section of your GET READY! binder.

Investment Income

Investments can pay annual income. If you have an investment that pays annual income, such as a dividend-paying stock, a bond, or a real estate investment trust (REIT), enter the information in **Table 58**. This information can be found in statements that you receive in the mail or online (if applicable).

Table 58: Investment Income

Name of investment source (CD, stocks, bonds, REIT)			
Type of income (dividend, interest, coupon, distribution)			
Annual distribution*			
As of date			
How income is paid			
Account to which income is deposited			
Beneficiary or survivor benefits? If yes, enter name			
Website and log-in credentials			
Location of documents*			
Notes:			

---

*NEXT STEPS

From the table above, enter your annual distribution in the income section of your cash flow statement (page 193). Store original account documents with your secure documents. Then, add your most recent annual statement to the income section of your GET READY! binder.

Retirement Income

Retirement is something we all look forward to, whether it's full retirement or just cutting back. If you've done a good job with saving for retirement, you'll reap the benefits. In **Table 59**, enter information on distributions that you are currently receiving from retirement plans. The information can be found on your statements from the income source.

Table 59: Retirement Income

Name of income source			
Type of income source (such as Social Security, IRA, pension, 401(k))			
Annual income*			
As of date			
How income is paid (and name of account if paid by auto-deposit)			
Date distributions started			
Distribution frequency			
Distribution option (single life, joint life, or other)			
Website and log-in credentials			
Document location*			
Notes:			

*NEXT STEPS

From the table above, enter your annual income into the income section of your cash flow statement (page 193). Store original documents with your secure documents. Add your most recent annual statement to the income section of your GET READY! binder.

Tip

In creating your financial calendar, it is important to note that if you take an early withdrawal from a retirement plan, prior to age 59 ½, you'll face an early withdrawal penalty of 10 percent in addition to any income taxes you may owe. There are some very specific exceptions, which you can find at https://www.irs.gov/retirement-plans/plan-participant-employee/retirement-topics-tax-on -early-distributions. And as discussed on page 77, when you take your Social Security benefits will affect your overall benefit.

END-OF-CHAPTER CHECK-IN

Did this chapter help you GET READY!? In the following table, assess your level of financial preparedness by checking the appropriate status box for all the topics in this chapter.

	In Progress	Completed	Not Applicable
Basic employment earnings information			
Cash compensation			
Paid time off			
Group (employee) benefits			
Total compensation			
Dependents coverage			
Other earned income			
Online income/sales			
Royalties			
Investment income			
Retirement income			

PRINT FORMS

To print these forms, visit my website at www.tonysteuer.com/resources.

NOTES

_____

_____

_____

_____

_____

_____

_____

CHAPTER 7

Organizing Your Debts, Personal Loans, Living Expenses, and Taxes

There's nothing inappropriate about having debt in America. It's what helped us grow over time. It's when debt gets out of control that you have to worry.
—WARREN BUFFETT

Emergency preparedness requires you to invest your time and money. Emergency supplies have to be purchased and maintained. Assembling a fully stocked first aid kit can cost between $200 and $300, and then you have the cost of whatever other equipment you deem necessary for your situation. If you purchase a kit for a family of three to have food and supplies for a few days, you'll spend another few hundred dollars. Specialized rescue equipment will cost you more. And your supplies will expire and need to be replaced, which creates an ongoing expense beyond the initial cost.

Throughout our lives, we will have many types of expenses, ranging from the necessary to the what is nice to have. All of us have expenses for the basics, such as food and housing. When our expenses, such as buying a house or car, are higher than we can afford or want to pay out of savings, we take out a loan. A loan is considered a liability and is any money that you owe to another person or entity (bank, credit union, or other lender). At some point, almost everyone will take out a loan, whether it's for education, a car, a house, or to meet some other expenses. Understanding and managing your loans and expenses will help you to reduce expense costs on your bills and on your loans.

GET READY!: ORGANIZING YOUR LOANS, DEBTS, TAXES, AND EXPENSES

In this chapter, we're going to review the areas where most of your money is spent: loans, taxes, and expenses. While organizing this part of the planner, you will learn about—

1. **Car loans and leases.** You will be making a list of any auto loans or leases. You'll also record information on the accounts themselves, along with their balances.

SECURED VS. UNSECURED LOANS

There are many types of loans available with a major difference being whether a loan is secured or unsecured:

- **Secured loans** require collateral, which means you must agree to use property/assets to guarantee the loan. If the loan is not paid back (default), the lender will take your collateral.

- **Unsecured loans** do not require collateral. Because there is no property to back up the loan, lenders will charge a higher interest rate.

FIXED VS. VARIABLE INTEREST RATES

Loans have two basic types of interest rates:

- **Fixed-rate loans** charge a set annual interest rate for a specific number of years, for example, 4 percent interest per year for 10 years.

- **Variable-rate loans** normally start with a reduced rate for a short period of time, called a "teaser rate," and then adjust to a market-rate index. Variable-rate loans are usually less expensive in the short term. Variable-rate loans have the potential of lower payments if interest rates are stable or go down. However, they also have the risk of higher payments if rates go up.

2. **Home mortgages.** You'll make an inventory of any mortgages and lines of credit on your primary home, vacation home, or time-share, including any reverse mortgages.

3. **Student loans.** You will be documenting your student loans.

4. **Other personal debt and business loans.** You'll gather information on any other loans that you have outstanding in your name, including investment loans, business loans, and any other personal loans.

5. **Credit cards.** You'll be able to add details about all of your credit cards, including details on rewards programs.

6. **Living expenses.** You'll be able to gather information on all of your ongoing living expenses ranging from rent and utilities to subscriptions and services.

7. **Taxes.** In this section, you'll add information on where your tax returns are located along with storage of tax documentation, adding details on any property taxes.

Having an overview of all of your expenses and loans can help you spot areas where you may have duplication or might find a way to reduce fees and other costs. If you can save 1 percent on your loans and expenses, that is an extra 1 percent that you will be saving each year.

Car Loans and Leases

While getting a new car can be a lot of fun, paying for it is a whole different matter. There are four basic ways to pay for a new car: cash with no financing, direct lending, dealership financing, and leasing. Take the time to know and understand the terms, conditions, and costs to finance a car before you sign a contract.

On the facing page, you can enter the details about your car loan(s) or lease(s) in **Table 60**. This information can be found in the loan contract provided by the lender or on your loan statements.

Table 60: Car Loans and Leases

	Car Loan (or Lease) 1	Car Loan (or Lease) 2
Make, model, and year of car (referred to as collateral)		
Loan or lease type		
Lending institution/ leasing agent's name		
Account #		
Original loan amount		
Originating date		
Loan or lease term and maturity date*		
As of date		
Interest rate		
Fixed or variable interest rate (if variable—how long is initial fixed period?)		
Loan balance*		
Loan or lease payment amount and frequency*		
How are loan statements received? (email or mail)		
How are payments made? (check, online, automatically)		
Late payment penalty		
Pre-payment penalty		
Website and log-in credentials		
Location of documents		
Notes:		

*NEXT STEPS

From the table above, enter the loan or lease payment in the expenses section of your cash flow statement (page 193). Enter the loan balance into the liabilities section of your net worth statement (page 199). Note the loan payoff (maturity) date or lease expiration date on your financial calendar (page 216). Keep the original loan documents with your secure documents. Then add a recent loan statement to the loans section of your GET READY! binder.

Note

When you lease a car, you have the right to use it for an agreed number of months and miles. Leasing has lower costs than directly buying a car, as the monthly payments on a lease are usually lower than monthly finance payments if you bought the same car. You are paying to drive the car, not buy it. That means you're paying for the car's expected depreciation during the lease period, plus a rent charge, taxes, and fees. When reviewing a lease, consider the following factors: agreed-upon value of the vehicle, costs at different points in the lease cycle, length of lease, and your annual estimated mileage. At the end of a lease, you must return the car unless the lease agreement lets you buy it.

Home Loan (Mortgage)

Buying a house is probably the largest purchase any of us will ever make. And usually buying a house entails taking out a mortgage on your house, and this mortgage will almost certainly be the largest loan you ever have. So it's important to consider all of your options when taking out a mortgage (primary home loan) and to make sure that you keep it on track. Choosing the wrong home mortgage or not making your payments can have significant repercussions, including the possible loss of your home, negative impact to your credit history, and possibly forcing bankruptcy.

Home Equity Loans (Second Mortgages)

This is a loan that allows you to borrow money using the equity in your home as collateral. Funds can be used to pay off major expenses such as home remodeling, education expenses, and medical bills, or for consolidating credit card debt. Since your house is used as collateral, the lender can foreclose on your home if you cannot repay the loan. Loan interest is no longer tax deductible under the 2017 Tax Act.

Note

There are two types of home equity loans:

- **Home equity loan:** A lump sum is borrowed on a one-time basis and usually has a fixed interest rate. Term is usually 3 to 15 years.
- **Home equity line of credit (HELOC):** A revolving line of credit that allows you to withdraw the funds at any time for more flexibility. These usually have adjustable interest rates. Term is usually 10 years.

On the facing page, enter details about your primary and secondary home loans as applicable in **Table 61**. This information can usually be found on your mortgage statements or on the original loan paperwork.

Table 61: Home Loan (Mortgage)

	Primary Mortgage	HELOC and Home Equity
Property address		
Loaning institution/lender name (current servicer)		
Account #		
Initial loan balance		
Originating date		
Loan term and maturity date*		
As of date		
Interest rate		
Interest rate fixed or adjustable (if adjustable, note date when rate may adjust)*		
Loan balance*		
Credit line (for HELOCs)		
Escrow balance		
Loan payment amount and frequency*		
Funds in suspense		
Late payment penalty		
Prepayment penalty		
Balloon payment (amount and date)		
How statements are received (mail or email)		
Method by which payments are paid (check or auto-pay, and if auto-pay, which account)		
Escrow payments: Homeowners insurance* Property tax* Mortgage insurance* HOA fees*		
Location of documents*		
Website and log-in credentials		
Notes:		

Continued on next page . . . ➡

Note

In the event of an emergency or disaster, you are still responsible for paying your mortgage, regardless of the condition of your house or its habitability. Proof of home ownership is usually required to receive federal disaster assistance. You will need to contact your lender for your mortgage or deed of trust if these documents are not stored with your secure documents or in your GET READY! binder.

Tip

If you are having trouble making your mortgage payments, take control by reaching out to your mortgage servicer and a HUD-approved housing counselor. This can help you maintain a positive credit history and keep your financial life in balance.

Private Mortgage Insurance

Private mortgage insurance, also called PMI, is a type of mortgage insurance you might be required to buy if you have a conventional loan. Like other kinds of mortgage insurance, PMI protects the lender—not you—if you stop making payments on your loan. PMI is arranged by the lender and provided by private insurance companies. PMI is usually required when you have a conventional loan and make a down payment of less than 20 percent of the home's purchase price. If you're refinancing with a conventional loan and your equity is less than 20 percent of the value of your home, PMI is also usually required. You should try to avoid PMI due to its cost, if possible. PMI fees vary from around 0.3 percent to about 1.5 percent of the original loan amount per year, depending on the size of the down payment and the borrower's credit score.

If you have PMI, enter details in **Table 62**. You can find this information from a recent mortgage statement or in your original documents.

Table 62: Private Mortgage Insurance

Property with PMI	
Insurer/lender (who you pay)	
Account or policy number	
Home purchase price	
Original mortgage balance	
Original loan-to-value ratio (divide original balance by purchase price)	
Premium* (and frequency)	
Method by which premiums are paid (check or auto-pay, and if auto-pay, which account)	
How statements are received (mail or email)	
As of date	
Current home appraised value	
Mortgage balance	
Loan-to-value (LTV) ratio (current): current mortgage balance divided by current appraised value*	
Location of documents*	
Website and log-in credentials	
Notes:	

*NEXT STEPS

From the table above, enter the premium payment in the expenses section of your cash flow statement (page 193). Enter a reminder on your financial calendar (page 216) to review the loan-to-value ratio annually (see tip on the following page). Keep the original loan documents with your secure documents. Then add a recent loan statement to the loans section of your GET READY! binder.

Tip

Keep track of the ratio between your loan balance and home value. When the loan-to-value ratio reaches 80 percent, you can contact your lender to cancel your PMI. When it drops to 78 percent, your lender is required to terminate it automatically. However, that is not always the case, so be sure to keep track of this yourself.

Vacation Home (Second Home) Loans

These are loans taken out on a vacation (second) home. Lenders will usually require that the property be a certain distance from the borrower's primary residence or that it be located in a resort or vacation area (such as near an ocean or a lake). These loans typically have a lower rate than investment property loans. Many lenders will not offer a second-home loan if the borrower intends to rent the property out for any period of time.

Time-Share and Vacation Club Loans

Time-share and vacation club loans differ from traditional mortgages in that these are personal loans made directly through a lender working with the developer. Most time-share sales are made after a presentation where there is high pressure to make an immediate purchase at a price that's only valid for that day. The average new time-share price is $20,000 (with a range from less than $10,000 to more than $85,000). Interest rates average 14 percent for a term of almost 10 years, according to the most recent statistics from the American Resort Development Association (ARDA).

In **Table 63**, add the applicable details for any vacation home and/or time-share loans. Information can be found on your loan statements or original loan documents.

Table 63: Vacation Home and Time-Share Loans

	Vacation Home	Time-Share
Property address		
Loaning institution/lender name (current servicer)		
Account #		
Original loan amount		
Originating date		
Loan term		
As of date		
Interest rate		

	Vacation Home	Time-Share
Interest rate fixed or adjustable (if adjustable, note date when rate may adjust)		
Loan balance*		
Escrow balance		
Final payment date		
Loan payment amount and frequency*		
How statements are received (mail or email)		
Funds in suspense		
Method by which payments are paid (check or auto-pay and if auto-pay, which account)		
Late payment penalty		
Prepayment penalty		
Balloon payment (amount and date)		

Escrow payments:
   Homeowners insurance*
   Property tax*
   Mortgage insurance*
   HOA fees*		

Location of documents*		
Web address and log-in credentials		
Notes:		

*NEXT STEPS

From the table above, enter the loan payment and total loan costs in the expenses section of your cash flow statement (page 193). If you are making escrow payments, enter the loan amount and escrow payment items in the corresponding sections of the cash flow statement. Enter the loan balance into the liabilities section of your net worth statement (page 199). Note the loan payoff (maturity) date on your financial calendar (page 216). Keep the original loan documents with your secure documents. Then add a recent loan statement to the loans section of your GET READY! binder.

Reverse Mortgage

With a reverse mortgage, you borrow money using your home as a guarantee for the loan, as you would for a traditional mortgage. Unlike a traditional mortgage, a reverse mortgage is repaid when the borrowers no longer live in the home. Although you won't make monthly mortgage payments, you'll need to continue to pay property taxes and homeowners insurance and keep your house in good condition, otherwise the lender can foreclose on your home. Because interest and fees are added to the loan balance each month, your loan balance goes up—not down—over time. As your loan balance increases, your home equity decreases. Reverse mortgage borrowers must be age 62 or older. Borrowers usually use the loan to help pay for living expenses. The Consumer Financial Protection Bureau has a useful discussion guide at https://www.consumerfinance.gov/documents/5204/cfpb_reverse-mortgage-discussion-guide.pdf.

There are three types of reverse mortgages:

- **Line of credit:** With a line of credit, you only pay interest on money you use. The amount of money available to you grows over time.
- **Monthly payout:** This can be a good choice if you need additional monthly income to cover daily living expenses. You can combine a monthly payout with a line of credit.
- **Lump sum payout:** Typically offers less money than other payout options. You will pay interest on your money even when you don't spend it, since you've "borrowed" it.

In **Table 64**, add details about your reverse mortgage, if applicable. You can find this information with your closing documents or on a recent statement.

Table 64: Reverse Mortgage

Property address	
Financial institution	
Contact information	
Type of reverse mortgage	
Loan #	
Effective date	
Who is listed on the loan?	
Payment plan (lump sum, line of credit, or monthly payout)	
As of date	
Loan balance*	

Set-asides (examples: repair, escrow for tax and insurance, service fee, first year property charges)	
Total available funds or line of credit (as applicable)	
Interest rate (daily periodic rate/monthly periodic rate/annual percentage rate)	
Interest rate change notice	
Finance charge current cycle (total amount of interest and mortgage insurance premium accrued)	
Total finance charges accrued	
Servicing fees current cycle	
Total servicing fees accrued	
Monthly payout* (if applicable)	
If monthly payout, how is it paid out and to which bank account? (check or bank draft)	
Is loan insured through the Federal Housing Authority Home Equity Conversion Mortgage Program?	
Lender website and log-in credentials	
Location of documents*	
Notes:	

---

*NEXT STEPS

From the table above, if you receive a monthly loan payout, enter it in the income section of your cash flow statement (page 193). Enter the loan balance into the liabilities section of your net worth statement (page 199). Keep the original loan documents with your secure documents. Then add a recent loan statement to the loans section of your GET READY! binder.

Tip

A reverse mortgage is not free money. It is a loan that you, or your heirs, will eventually have to pay back, usually by selling your home. Borrowed money + interest + fees each month = rising loan balance. Also, if you are married, be sure both spouses are listed; otherwise, if the spouse who took out the reverse mortgage passes away, the other spouse could lose the home.

Student Loans

Student loans are now commonly used to help pay for higher education expenses. Students and parents borrow funds that must be repaid with interest. Loans are available from a variety of sources, including the federal government, individual state governments, public and private agencies and organizations, and the institutions themselves. According to thecollegesolution.com, roughly two out of three students borrow money to pay for college, and the typical student borrower will owe approximately $37,000.

 Tip

Before borrowing money, consider whether you can qualify for grants, scholarships, the GI Bill, or some type of work study. Borrowing money for education should be your last option. There are grants and scholarships for all types of circumstances beyond income, such as ethnicity, health issues, and sports. A good resource sponsored by the US Department of Labor is https://www.careeronestop .org/toolkit/training/find-scholarships.aspx. It's also important to consider if the cost of a big-name university as compared to an equivalent education at a state college is worth the added expense.

 Tip

Loans vary as to the terms of the loan and the interest rate. So be sure to compare options. There are two basic types of college loans: federal and non-federal private loans. Your first choice for borrowing for education should be federal student loans; max out these before considering private student loans. Federal student loans are usually cheaper than private loans, as federal loans may be subsidized and offer more flexible repayment terms. Fill out the Free Application for Financial Student Aid (FAFSA) to be eligible for any federal student loans, work study, or grants. You can learn more about FAFSA by visiting https://fafsa.ed.gov.

In **Table 65**, enter information on your student loan(s), as applicable. You should be able to locate this information on your loan statement and original loan documents. If you have more than two student loans, use the Notes section at the end of this chapter.

Table 65: Student Loans

	Student Loan 1	Student Loan 2
Loan provider name (contact info)		
Loan type		
Account #		
Initial amount borrowed		

	Student Loan 1	Student Loan 2
Loan payoff date		
As of date		
Current loan balance*		
Payment* (and frequency)		
Payment method (check, online, auto draft account)		
How statements are received (mail, email)		
Interest rate		
Fixed or variable interest rate		
Loan payoff amount		
Location of documents*		
Loan servicer website and log-in credentials		
Notes:		

*NEXT STEPS

From the table above, enter the loan payment in the expenses section of your cash flow statement (page 193). Enter the loan balance into the liabilities section of your net worth statement (page 199). Note the loan payoff (maturity) date on your financial calendar (page 216). Keep the original loan documents with your secure documents. Then add a recent loan statement to the loans section of your GET READY! binder.

Tip

If you are struggling with repaying student loans, consider the following ways to help you (be sure to consider all pros and cons):

- **Consolidation:** Many loan service providers allow you to consolidate similar types of loans into a single loan, which may allow you to get a lower interest rate. See Debt Consolidation Loans discussion on page 128.

- **Restructure your monthly payments:** Regardless of whether your loan is federal or private, options most likely exist to change your payment structure to fit your financial situation. Federal borrowers can apply for income-based repayment plans like Pay As You Earn (PAYE) or Income-Based Repayment (IBR). Private borrowers often have fewer options than federal borrowers, and the options available can vary significantly from lender to lender. You will have to contact your lending institution to learn whether you can adjust the terms of your loan. The Consumer Financial Protection Bureau (CFPB) has some good resources at https://www.consumer finance.gov/ask-cfpb/what-is-pay-as-you-earn-paye-how-do-i-know-if-i-qualify-en-1555/.

Investment Property Loans

Investment property loans usually have higher interest rates and require a larger down payment than properties occupied by their owners as second homes. If you will be renting out your second home (vacation home) for part of the year, you will most likely be required to take out an investment property loan. Be sure to make your intentions clear to the lender so you wind up with the right type of loan.

In **Table 66**, you can add details for any investment property loans that you may have. Information can be found on your statements or original loan documents.

Table 66: Investment Property Loans

	Investment Property Loan 1	Investment Property Loan 2
Property address		
Lender name (current servicer)		
Account #		
Original loan amount		
Originating date		
Loan term		
As of date		
Interest rate		
Interest rate fixed or adjustable (if adjustable, note date when rate may adjust)		
Loan balance*		
Escrow balance		
Final payment (payoff) date*		
Loan payment amount and frequency*		
How payments are made (mail, online, auto-pay, and account)		

	Investment Property Loan 1	Investment Property Loan 2
How statements are received (mail, online, other)		
Funds in suspense		
Late payment penalty		
Pre-payment penalty		
Balloon payment (amount and date)		
Escrow payments: Homeowners insurance* Property tax* Mortgage insurance* HOA fees*		
Location of documents*		
Lender website and log-in credentials		
Notes:		

*NEXT STEPS

From the table above, enter the loan payment and total loan costs in the expenses section of your cash flow statement (page 193). Enter the loan balance into the liabilities section of your net worth statement (page 199). Note the loan payoff (maturity) date on your financial calendar (page 216). Keep the original loan documents with your secure documents. Then add a recent loan statement to the loans section of your GET READY! binder.

Business (Commercial) Property Loan

A commercial real estate loan lets you purchase or refinance an owner-occupied business property or expand or remodel an existing facility. If you own the property free and clear, you can also use a commercial real estate loan to leverage your equity to finance a variety of business needs.

In **Table 67,** you can add details for any business (commercial) property loan that you are personally responsible for. Information can be found on your statements or original loan documents.

Table 67: Business (Commercial) Property Loan

Property address	
Lender name (current servicer)	
Account #	
Original loan amount	
Originating date	
Loan term	
As of date	
Interest rate	
Interest rate fixed or adjustable (if adjustable, note date when rate may adjust)	
Loan balance*	
Escrow balance	
Final payment (payoff) date*	
Loan payment amount and frequency*	
How payments are made (mail, online, auto-pay, and account)	
How statements are received (mail, online, other)	
Funds in suspense	
Late payment penalty	
Prepayment penalty	
Balloon payment (amount and date)	
Escrow payments: Homeowners insurance* Property tax* Mortgage insurance* HOA fees*	
Location of documents*	
Lender website and log-in credentials	
Notes:	

Personal Debts and Loans

There are many types of loans and debts that you might incur over the years. You may owe money after buying a boat, working out an agreement with the Internal Revenue Service, getting a payday loan, owing money to a friend, or receiving a legal judgment.

In **Table 68**, add in the applicable information about any miscellaneous personal debts and loans that you have. Depending on the loan type, if you have borrowed money with a company, you will have loan documents and statements, while if you have borrowed money from a friend, you may only have a written agreement.

Table 68: Personal Debts and Loans

Name of lender/entity owed		
Type of loan (personal, boat, tax, or legal adjustment)		
Contact information (phone and address)		
Account #		
Origination date		
Original balance		
As of date		
Current balance*		
Payment amount and frequency*		
Finance rate/interest rate		
Is rate fixed or adjustable? (and if adjustable, when)		
Loan term/payoff date		
Late payment date (and penalty)		

Continued on next page . . .

How payments are made (mail, online, auto-pay, and account)		
How statements are received (mail, online, other)		
Web address and log-in credentials		
Location of documents*		
Notes:		

*NEXT STEPS

From the table above, enter the loan payment and total loan costs in the expenses section of your cash flow statement (page 193). Enter the loan balance into the liabilities section of your net worth statement (page 199). Note the loan payoff (maturity) date on your financial calendar (page 216). Keep the original loan documents with your secure documents. Then add a recent loan statement to the loans section of your GET READY! binder.

Credit Cards

When a credit card is issued, the bank backing the card will provide you with a credit line (amount of credit available to you). You can make purchases up to your credit limit while having a grace period during which you can pay off the balance without incurring any interest charges. After this initial period, your credit card balance will start to accrue interest, usually at very high interest rates. Carrying a balance on a credit card is one of the most expensive ways of borrowing money.

In **Table 69**, add details regarding your credit cards. Most of the information should be on your credit card statement, and the rest you should be able to access online or with documentation provided when the credit card was issued.

Table 69: Credit Cards

Card name (Ex: Bank of America)			
Type of card (Ex: Visa, MasterCard, Amex, other)			
Brand (store, sponsoring organization, association, other)			
Issuing bank			

Debit or credit?				
Name on card				
Primary card holder				
Card number				
Expiration date				
Security code				
Debit card PIN				
As of date				
Credit limit				
Total outstanding balance*				
Average monthly payment*				
Payment due date (day of the month)				
Annual fee*				
How payments are made (mail, online, auto-pay, and account)				
How statements are received (mail, online, other)				
Grace period on payments				
Annual/daily periodic rate (interest charged daily)				
If special introductory offer, list expiration date*				
Rewards/benefits (note rewards that vary by type of transaction)				
Reward status				
Rewards expiration date(s)*				
Phone # to call if card is lost or stolen				

Continued on next page . . . ➡

Location of card				
Location of documents				
Website and log-in credentials				
Notes:				

*NEXT STEPS —————————————————————————————

From the table above, enter the monthly credit card payments and annual fees in the expenses section of your cash flow statement (page 193). Enter the loan balance into the liabilities section of your net worth statement (page 199). Note the expiration date of special introductory rate offers and reward expiration dates on your financial calendar (page 216). Keep the original credit card documents with your secure documents. Then add a recent statement to the loans section of your GET READY! binder.

Tip

There are thousands of credit cards available to you. When reviewing your credit cards, it's important to review different options. Choose your credit card wisely, as there are major differences between credit cards, including account fees, interest rates, finance charges, and reward benefits. The Federal Trade Commission (FTC) has a Guide to Credit Cards (http://www.consumer.ftc.gov/articles/0332-credit-debit-and-charge-cards). See as well the Q&A on how to shop for a credit card from the Consumer Financial Protection Bureau (CFPB) at http://www.consumerfinance.gov/blog/how-do-i-shop-for-a-credit-card.

Debt Consolidation Loans

Debt consolidation loans are often misleading and should be avoided. A debt consolidation loan is simply combining multiple loans and debt obligations into one loan with the claim of a lower interest rate with reduced monthly plans. It is actually a refinanced loan with an extended repayment period, which means it will take longer to pay off your debt, and it does not mean that your outstanding debt amount is reduced.

The bottom line is this: Debt consolidation plans are ranked as the top consumer complaint received by the Federal Trade Commission. You'll be better off reviewing your cash flow and making adjustments to your spending and, if possible, your income, and paying off your debt as soon as you can. Before proceeding with a debt consolidation plan, you may want to contact a credit counseling service accredited with either the National Foundation for Credit Counseling (NFCC) at http://www.nfcc.org or the Financial Counseling Association of America (FCAA) at http://www.fcaa.org.

In **Table 70**, you can add details on any debt consolidation loans or other debt settlement plans that you may have. This information can be found on your monthly statement or in the original lending documentation that you received when you were granted the loan.

Table 70: Debt Consolidation Loans

Name of lender/entity owed	
Contact information (phone and address)	
Account #	
Origination date	
Original balance	
As of date	
Current balance*	
Payment amount and frequency*	
How are statements received?	
How are payments made? If auto-pay, from what account?	
Annual fee (and other fees)	
Finance rate/interest rate	
Is rate fixed or adjustable? (If adjustable, when?)	
Loan term/payoff date	
Late payment date (and penalty)	
Website and log-in credentials	
Location of documents*	
Notes:	

*NEXT STEPS

From the table above, enter the monthly payment and total loan costs in the expenses section of your cash flow statement (page 193). Enter the loan balance into the liabilities section of your net worth statement (page 199). Note the loan payoff (maturity) date on your financial calendar (page 216). Keep the original loan documents with your secure documents. Then add a recent loan statement to the loans section of your GET READY! binder.

Tip

If you have a debt consolidation plan, then just plan to follow the terms and, if possible, pay it off early. And consider that there may be better options to refinance the loan, such as a home equity line of credit, if you own a home. Basically, whenever you can, refinance high-interest-rate loans into lower-interest-rate loans.

Living Expenses
Renting and Leasing a Residence

In **Table 71**, you can enter details if you are renting or leasing your residence. This information should be located on your monthly statement (if applicable) and on your rental (or lease) agreement.

Table 71: Renting or Leasing a Residence

Address	
Name of person/company that you are renting from and contact information	
Date agreement started	
Monthly rent (or lease) payment*	
Date rental (or lease) agreement terminates	
How are statements received?	
How are payments made? If auto-pay, from what account?	
Website and log-in credentials	
Location of documents	
Notes:	

*NEXT STEPS

From the table above, enter the monthly payment in the expenses section of your cash flow statement (page 193). Note the agreement termination date on your financial calendar (page 216). Keep the original loan documents with your secure documents. Then add a recent statement to the loans section of your GET READY! binder.

Tip

Proof of housing rental may be required to receive federal disaster assistance, so be sure to keep a copy with your secure documents and/or your GET READY! binder. If you need a copy of your lease or rental agreement, ask your property owner for a copy.

Utility and Household Bills

Add details to **Table 72** about your ongoing utility and household expenses. Information to complete this can be found on your monthly statements.

Table 72: Utility and Household Bills

	Company Name, Website, Log-In Credentials	Account #	Average Monthly Payment	How Bills Arrive (mail or email) and Are Paid (check or auto-pay—note auto-pay account)
Cable/satellite TV				
Electric				
Garbage				
Gardener/ landscaping				
Gas				
Heating oil/ propane				
Homeowners association				
Home security (alarm company, other)				
Housecleaning				
HVAC (heating, vents, and air conditioning)				
Internet				
Pest control				
Phone (cellular)				
Phone (landline)				

Continued on next page . . .

	Company Name, Website, Log-In Credentials	Account #	Average Monthly Payment	How Bills Arrive (mail or email) and Are Paid (check or auto-pay— note auto-pay account)
Pool maintenance				
Septic				
Transportation 1				
Transportation 2				
Water/sewer				
Other				
Notes:				

> **NEXT STEPS**
>
> From the table above, add the monthly payments to your cash flow statement (page 193). A recent statement for each service should be kept in the loans and expenses section of your GET READY! binder.

Education, Care, and Support: Child Care, Day Care, Tuition, and Adult Care

Over our lives, there are many types of education and care that are required. This ranges from toddlers requiring child care, to preschoolers attending day care, to children attending private school and eventually college. And for some of us, care costs may include supporting a parent or other relative.

In **Table 73**, enter information about these services and their costs. You can find this information on billing statements or agreements.

Table 73: Education, Care, and Support: Child Care, Day Care, Tuition, and Adult Care

Name of person (receiving education, care, or support)			
Relationship			
Name of education or care provider			
Date started			

Date contract/obligation will terminate*			
As of date			
Current payments and frequency*			
How statements are received (mail, email)			
How bills are paid (check, auto-deduct—add account)			
Location of documents*			
Website and log-in credentials			
Notes:			

*NEXT STEPS

From the table above, add the monthly payments to your cash flow statement (page 193). Add contract/obligation termination date to your financial calendar (page 216). Store original agreements and contracts with your secure documents. A recent statement for each service should be kept in the loans and expenses section of your GET READY! binder.

Subscriptions and Services

There are many subscriptions and services that we can subscribe to, including those that are offline, such as magazines, or online, such as music-streaming services; some services combine both the physical and digital worlds, such as the major newspapers. In **Table 74**, add information about your various subscriptions and services, both online and offline, as applicable. You can also add details about the accounts in the space provided.

Table 74: Subscriptions and Services

	Company Name, Website, Log-In Credentials	Account # and Registration ID	Average Monthly Payment	How Bills Arrive (mail or email) and Are Paid (check or auto-pay—note auto-pay account)
Newspapers (digital and physical)				
Magazines and periodicals (physical and digital)				

Continued on next page . . .

	Company Name, Website, Log-In Credentials	Account # and Registration ID	Average Monthly Payment	How Bills Arrive (mail or email) and Are Paid (check or auto-pay— note auto-pay account)
Cloud storage (such as Box and Dropbox)				
General web service (such as Amazon and Apple iCloud)				
Music streaming (such as iTunes and Pandora)				
Video streaming (such as Netflix, Hulu, Redbox)				
Gaming (such as Xbox Live and Steam)				
Food and delivery services (such as Blue Apron and Amazon Fresh)				
Software subscriptions (such as Microsoft Office and anti-virus)				
Membership sites (such as Match.com)				
Other				
Notes:				

NEXT STEPS

From the table above, enter the average monthly payments in the expenses section of your cash flow statement (page 193). Keep any original documents with your secure documents. Then add a recent statement into your GET READY! binder in the loans and expenses section.

Memberships, Season Tickets, Clubs, and Organizations

During each of our lives, we join and participate in many clubs and organizations. In **Table 75**, you can enter information on any paid memberships, season tickets, clubs, and organizations that you may belong to. This information can be found on billing statements or on your original membership documents.

Table 75: Memberships, Season Tickets, Clubs, and Organizations

	Organization Name, Website, Log-In Credentials	Account #/ Membership #	Average Monthly Payment (or dues)	How Bills Arrive (mail or email) and Are Paid (check or auto-pay— note auto-pay account)
Auto club (AAA)				
Gym				
Service club				
Season tickets				
Other				
Notes:				

> **NEXT STEPS**
>
> Add the total monthly payments from the table above to your cash flow statement in the expenses section (page 193). Original agreements and documents should be stored with your secure documents; add a recent statement to the assets section of your GET READY! binder.

Taxes

It is said that two things in life are certain: death and taxes. In this section, we'll take a look at your taxes. Keeping organized records during your lifetime will help you with filing your taxes and making matters easier for your family.

In **Table 76,** add information about your tax return, including how you file. This will help you prepare your tax returns and will help your heirs, as they will need to file a final tax return for you.

Table 76: Taxes

	Federal Tax Return	State Tax Return (if applicable)
Name(s) on tax return		
Filing status		
How do you prepare returns? (Turbo Tax, tax preparation service, CPA, other)		
How do you file returns? (digital or paper)		
Name and contact information (for tax preparation service, CPA, or other)		
If using online service, include website and log-in credentials		
Estimated taxes* (average)		
IRS and state websites and log-in credentials		
Location of documents* (tax returns and supporting information)		
Notes:		

*NEXT STEPS

From the table above, enter your average estimated tax payments in the expenses section of your cash flow statement (page 193). Estimated tax due dates are already listed in your financial calendar (page 216). Keep the original tax documents with your secure documents. Then add a recent tax return to the loans section of your GET READY! binder.

Note

Estimated taxes must be paid on income that is not subject to withholding for both federal and state income taxes (if your state has an income tax). This includes income from self-employment, interest, and dividends. You may also have to pay estimated tax if the amount of income tax being withheld from your salary, pension, or other income is not enough.

Note estimated tax due dates on your financial calendar (page 216). The year is divided into four periods to pay estimated tax. Each period has a specific payment deadline, typically April 15, June 15, September 15, and January 15 of the next year (unless the 15th falls on the weekend, in which case the due date is usually the following Monday (check www.irs.gov and your state tax bureau to confirm).

Tax Documents

Employers, investment firms, and banks, among others, will send you tax forms and statements that contain information you need to file your taxes if they have sent a payment to you. For certain financial transactions, you should keep appropriate documents such as donation receipts.

In **Table 77,** note which of the following documents you usually receive each year. This will help you keep track of your incoming tax documents and help your heirs file any final tax returns.

Table 77: Tax Documents

	How You Receive (mail or electronically, and to which email address)
W-2: issued by your employer	
1099-MISC: usually for contract work and/or income for which taxes were not withheld	
1099-K: usually for freelance income processed through a third-party network such as PayPal or from Uber or Lyft	
1099-INT: interest income	
1099-DIV: dividend income and distributions from investments	
1099-R: pension, IRA, and annuity income	
1099-G: state income tax refund and/or unemployment insurance income	
1099-B or 1099-S: income from the sale of stocks and other investments	
1099-SSA: Social Security income	
K-1: income from a partnership, limited liability company, S Corporation, or other entity	
W-2G: gambling winnings; you should also have records proving gambling expenses	
Other tax forms regularly received	

Tip

Employers and companies paying contractors are required to send out W-2s and 1099-Misc forms by January 31. Many companies are now opting to send them electronically rather than through the mail, so make sure your information is updated. If you haven't received expected forms by the third week of February, contact the organization. When you receive your forms, review them for accuracy. Mistakes happen, and you'll want to correct them as quickly as possible. If there are mistakes, the issuing organization needs to correct the problem and send you a new form.

Property Taxes

If you own a home or other property, you will have to pay property taxes in most states. In **Table 78**, add information on any property taxes you pay each year.

Table 78: Property Taxes

	Property 1	Property 2
Property address		
Taxable (assessed value)		
As of date		
Payment due date(s)*		
Annualized tax payment due*		
Breakdown of tax payments		
How statements are received		
How taxes are paid (mail, online)		
Tax authority website and log-in credentials		
Location of statements*		
Notes:		

*NEXT STEPS

From the table above, enter your annualized tax payment(s) listed in the table in the expenses section of your cash flow statement on page 193. Property tax due dates should be recorded in your financial calendar on page 216. Property tax statements should be kept with the rest of your tax return documentation and a copy of your most recent property tax statement added to the loans and expenses section of your GET READY! binder.

Tip

If your property value decreases, you can usually request that your property be reassessed to determine if your property tax can be reduced. You can use an online service like www.zillow.com to see comparable home-price values and an estimate on your own home.

Note

In the Notes section at the end of this chapter, add details about any other tax returns that you've filed, such as business or gift tax returns, where they are located, and if there was a tax preparer, along with any applicable contact information.

END-OF-CHAPTER CHECK-IN

Did this chapter help you GET READY!? In the following table, assess your level of financial preparedness by checking the appropriate status box for all the topics in this chapter.

	In Progress	Completed	Not Applicable
Car loans and leases			
Primary home loan			
Vacation home and time-share loans			
Reverse mortgage			
Student loans			
Investment and business property loans			
Personal loans and debts (miscellaneous)			
Credit cards			
Living expenses			
Education, care, and support (child care, day care, tuition, and adult care)			
Subscriptions and services			
Memberships, season tickets, clubs, and organizations			
Taxes			

PRINT FORMS

To print these forms, visit my website at www.tonysteuer.com/resources.

NOTES

CHAPTER 8

Assembling Your Insurance Portfolio

An ounce of prevention is worth a pound of cure.
—Benjamin Franklin

While you can be prepared for an emergency, you can't predict with certainty the type of emergency you will encounter or the resources you will need. When you put together an emergency kit or a first aid kit, you hope you'll never have to use it. But life is uncertain and things happen, and your emergency kit needs to be stocked with tools to address all types of situations. If you don't have the right tools, you may not be able to deal with a specific situation.

Insurance works in the same way by protecting your financial life. Insurance exists to help protect you for most types of risks. Like the first aid kit, you hope you don't need to use it; however, if you do, you'll be glad you have it.

On the pages that follow, you'll be able to review the different types of insurance and add information about the current coverage that you have.

 GET READY!: ASSEMBLING YOUR INSURANCE PORTFOLIO

In this chapter, we're going to take a look at your insurance portfolio. While organizing this part of the planner, you will learn about—

1. **Auto insurance.** You will be adding details about your auto insurance policies.

2. **Disability insurance.** You'll make an inventory of any disability insurance that you have, whether it's through an employer, individually, or both.

3. **Health insurance.** Here you will document the details about your health insurance—whether you have coverage through an employer, as an individual, or through a Medicare program.

4. **Homeowners and renters insurance.** I'll also ask you to gather information about your homeowners or renters insurance along with related property coverage such as earthquake and flood insurance.

5. **Life insurance.** You'll also be able to add details about your employer-provided and individual life insurance coverage.

6. **Long-term care insurance.** I will prompt you to add details about your long-term care insurance coverage.

7. **Annuities.** You'll be able to take information from your annuity statements and document it in this section.

8. **Other insurance coverage.** You can also document any other type of insurance that you have, such as Accidental Death & Dismemberment coverage, identity theft coverage, and any personal umbrella coverage.

Insurance is often overlooked in its role as the base of a sound financial plan. Insurance premiums can be a household's largest expense when all of the premiums are grouped together. Insurance is a way to protect yourself against a specific risk. If you are faced with a devastating loss of life, health, income, home, or auto, having the right insurance in place can make a huge difference. Take control by educating yourself and using that knowledge to obtain the appropriate insurance and to save on your insurance premiums.

 Note

The financial strength of an insurance company is highly important because an insurance policy is a long-term commitment. Third-party agencies rate insurance companies on a regular basis and offer their ratings and analysis online for free. However, some insurance companies are not rated by all of the rating services.

There are four main rating agencies, and each agency's rating system varies in its stringency and methodology:

- AM Best: www.ambest.com
- Fitch: www.fitchratings.com
- Moody's: www.moodys.com
- Standard & Poor's: www.standardandpoors.com

Auto Insurance

Auto insurance is required by most states. Check with your state's Department of Insurance to find out if your state requires coverage and, if so, at what amount. If you have a car loan, your lender will also have minimum coverage standards. If your state does not require auto insurance, you still should consider the coverage anyway, as the cost of not having the coverage can be very high.

Visit: https://tonysteuer.com/resources/insurance-regulatory-agencies to locate your state's Department of Insurance website and contact information.

Note

Each insurance company uses its own method to calculate your premium. Premiums depend on several key factors, including driving record, age, gender, marital status, type of vehicle, where you live, vehicle annual use, and previous claims.

In **Table 79**, enter details regarding your auto insurance. These details can be found on the declarations pages that you receive at renewal or on the policy.

Table 79: Auto Insurance

	Car 1	Car 2
Car insured		
Company name		
Policy number		
Issue date		
As of date		
Policy period*		
Principal driver		
Liability: bodily injury		
Liability: property damage		
Medical payments		
Comprehensive deductible and limits		
Collision deductible and limits		
Uninsured motor vehicle: bodily injury limits		
Uninsured motor vehicle: property damage		
Deductible		
Co-payment		
Premium (and frequency)*		
Premium last paid		

Continued on next page . . .

	Car 1	Car 2
Policy last reviewed		
How bills are received		
How premiums are paid		
Riders		
Discounts		
Agent name and contact info		
Location of policy and documents		
Web address and log-in credentials		
Notes:		

*NEXT STEPS

From the table above, add the premiums to the expenses section of your cash flow statement on page 193. Add the policy expiration date to your financial calendar on page 216. Your insurance policy can be stored with your important documents, and your declaration (data) pages (or copies) should go in the insurance section of your GET READY! binder.

Tip

Insurance companies offer a range of discounts if you meet requirements, such as bundling policies, putting multiple vehicles under one policy, having airbags, having anti-theft devices, taking a defensive driver course, and driving safely. Be sure to inquire each year when your policy is up for renewal or if you are shopping for new coverage elsewhere.

Tip

When you receive your car insurance policy renewal, do the following:

- **Check for changes.** Compare the policy renewal language with your existing policy to catch any changes in coverage or price. If there are changes, call your insurer to find out why.
- **Re-evaluate your needs.** If you are driving fewer miles per week than you had been, you might be eligible for a lower insurance rate. Likewise, if you have an older car, you may decide you can do without optional collision coverage. You may be paying more than your car is worth. Examples of circumstance changes that may impact your auto insurance premiums include a switch to working from home (rather than at an office) and having children that reach driving age (teenagers are much more expensive than adults).

- **Compare providers.** In addition to getting a quote from your current insurance provider, seek quotes online or by phone from several competitors.

- **Choose the policy that offers the best value.** Do not focus on price alone but on the amount of coverage offered for that price. Compare items such as deductibles, exclusions, and coverage limits.

- **Raise the deductible on collision and comprehensive coverages.** If you have an old car with a low cash value, you might want to drop these coverages altogether.

- **Make sure your information is accurate and up-to-date.** Your car insurance company will determine your rates based on factors such as your age, driving record, credit history, and location. You may be eligible for a lower rate if you have recently modified your driving habits.

Disability Insurance

Disability insurance provides income in the event that you become disabled. If you have an income that you are dependent on, then you have a need for disability insurance. A major point to consider is that you do not have to be completely or permanently disabled to receive benefits from a disability income insurance policy. Your chances of becoming disabled for more than 90 days before the age of 65 are quite high, ranging from close to 50 percent at 25 to 40 percent at age 45.

Note

There are three main types of disability income insurance, including—

- **Individual disability income insurance:** Coverage that you purchase directly from an insurance company. These policies will usually provide more coverage, as they include all earned income (including bonuses and commissions) and higher maximum coverage ($20,000 a month in benefits or more). Benefits are paid on an after-tax basis and so are not subject to income tax.

- **Employer/group long-term disability insurance:** Your employer will provide a basic coverage amount, and you may be automatically enrolled or you will be given the option to join at your employer's open enrollment period. Employers will sometimes offer the option of paying on a pre-tax or post-tax basis. If you pay on a pre-tax basis, your benefits will be subject to income tax. If you pay on an after-tax basis, your benefits will not be subject to income tax.

- **Social Security Disability Income Insurance (SSDI):** The Social Security Administration (SSA) provides long-term disability benefits based on your salary and the number of years you have worked and contributed to the Social Security system. Social Security replaces only a limited portion of your salary, and the qualifications to receive benefits are very strict. To learn more about SSDI and to read Social Security's fact sheets and actuarial publications, go to www.ssa.gov/disability.

In **Table 80**, add information about your group and individual disability income insurance policies. This information can be found in annual statements (if sent by company), your benefit confirmation (if through an employer), or in the policy (if individual coverage). If you have more than one individual policy, you can combine the information or re-label the columns.

Table 80: Disability Insurance

	Short-Term Disability Insurance	Group Long-Term Disability Insurance	Individual Long-Term Disability Insurance
Insurance company name			
Policy number			
If group, name of employer or group			
Issue date			
As of date			
Monthly benefit			
Benefit period			
Elimination period (waiting period)			
If group insurance— percentage of income covered: Monthly cap: (maximum) Compensation covered: (all, salary only?)			
Premium* (and frequency)			
Premium last paid			
Policy last reviewed			
How bills are received (mail, email)			
How premiums are paid (mail, online)			
Riders			
Ratings and/or exclusions			
Agent name & contact info			
Location of policy and documents			
Website and log-in credentials			
Notes:			

Tip

If you have group disability coverage, it's important to calculate the "actual" amount of coverage so that you will know what to expect in the event you are disabled. This will also help you gauge if you should have supplemental individual disability insurance coverage.

Step 1: Gross earnings covered (may be salary only): $_____

Step 2: Multiply by benefit percentage ____% = Monthly benefit: $_____ (if this exceeds your group LTD monthly cap of $_____, use monthly maximum cap for step 3)

Step 3: After-tax monthly benefit if employer pays premiums: Subtract gross income tax rate from lower of monthly benefit or monthly cap from step 2: $_____

Step 4: Multiply total cash compensation (salary, bonuses, and commissions) $_____ by 70% = $_____

Step 5: Amount that may be available as supplemental individual coverage: Subtract after-tax monthly benefit (step 3) from step 4 result: $_____.

Tip

When you review your disability insurance policy, consider the following:

- **Exclusions.** Sometimes a disability policy is issued with an exclusion for a certain illness or injury. The exclusion can be removed after a certain period. For example, if you have knee surgery, the insurance company may exclude any disabilities related to the knee for a certain period of time. However, the insurance companies will not usually remove this automatically. You will need to request to have this exclusion removed.

- **Future-purchase option or future-increase options.** Do you have these? When is it available, and are you eligible? Know the terms and be sure to take advantage if you are eligible. The insurance companies will typically notify you, although there is no guarantee that they will.

Health Insurance and Health Care Costs

Health insurance is a way to pay for health care by pooling your premiums with others who are insured. It provides coverage for medical expenses that can include illnesses, injuries, and chronic conditions, with the goal of giving you access to medical care and preventive care.

Health insurance comes in a variety of forms, so it's important to understand the terms of your coverage to ensure that you have a plan with the benefits that meet your needs. The individual health insurance marketplace continues to be unsettled. The Affordable Care Act (ACA) brought major changes to the individual health insurance market, including standardization of benefits and elimination of underwriting. Many changes have occurred since its inception, and it is highly likely that more changes are to come. Therefore, you should continually monitor your health insurance and review your options.

Note

It is important to be aware of your choice of networks. *If you go outside the HMO or PPO network of providers, you may have to pay a portion or all of the cost.* The following are the basic types of health insurance networks:

- **Health Maintenance Organization (HMO).** Coverage is usually limited to care from doctors who work for or contract with the HMO. This type of plan generally won't cover out-of-network care except in an emergency. All care is coordinated through the primary care physician, and you are required to get a referral to see a specialist. These plans feature lower co-payments and usually have the lowest premiums.

- **Preferred Provider Organization (PPO).** PPOs allow you the most freedom to use doctors, hospitals, and providers outside of the network without a referral for an additional cost. However, there is a higher cost for using an out-of-network provider. You are not required to get a referral to see a specialist. PPO plans usually have the highest premiums.

- **Exclusive Provider Organization (EPO).** A managed-care plan in which services are covered only if you use doctors, specialists, or hospitals in the plan's network (except in an emergency). You can see a specialist without a referral. Out-of-network physicians are not covered. EPO premiums are generally less expensive than PPO premiums and more expensive than HMO premiums.

- **Point of Service (POS).** Under this type of plan, you would select a primary care physician from an HMO-style network who will coordinate your care. You then also have access to a PPO network of doctors, hospitals, and other health care providers that belong to the plan's network.

Your health insurance options will also depend on your age. If you are under the age of 65, health insurance is available either through a group health insurance plan, typically offered by an employer, or through the individual health insurance market. If you are 65 or older, you have Medicare insurance and possibly Medicare supplements. There are some limited exceptions in which someone under the age of 65 can get Medicare. If you have Medicare, please go to page 149.

Short-Term Health Insurance Plans

Short-term health insurance plans provide limited health care coverage for a temporary gap in insurance. For example, policies may exclude maternity leave and mental health care. Short-term health insurance may also have limits that regular insurance coverage does not, such as a cap on the maximum benefits paid. The maximum coverage period is up to 364 days. However, you can purchase a new policy once a current policy terminates as long as the total duration of a single plan does not exceed 36 months.

Dental Insurance

Dental insurance provides coverage for dental care. Dental plans are typically structured like health insurance plans, including dental HMOs and dental PPOs. Dental plans are usually offered through employers. Individuals can also purchase dental insurance with premiums from $15 to $50 a month. Coverage usually has an annual maximum of $1,500, so it is not extensive. When reviewing plans, check if there is a waiting period before coverage starts and what the plan pays for, such as lab and material costs for crowns or bridges. It's important to note that dental discount programs are not dental insurance plans; they provide discounts (savings) rather than insurance benefits. Some insurance companies offer dental discount programs rather than dental insurance.

Vision Insurance

Vision insurance provides coverage for regular eye exams, eyeglasses, and contact lenses. Elective vision-corrective surgery may be covered under a vision insurance plan. Medically necessary major eye procedures such as cataract surgery are typically covered through health insurance plans. Vision insurance is often offered by employers. Premiums can range from $15 to $50 per month for individual vision insurance policies. Be sure to compare the benefits provided. All health insurance plans include vision insurance for children under the age of 18.

Medicare

Medicare is a federal health insurance program for Americans above the age of 65, along with people with certain disabilities. As of 2015, Medicare provided health insurance for more than 55 million people. Anyone above the age of 65 can buy Medicare, regardless of their income level. The only restriction is that you must have worked approximately 10 years to qualify for Medicare, which is defined as about 40 work credits, and a worker's spouse can qualify on the worker's record if they do not have enough credits of their own. It is important to note that Medicare consists of several components that eligible Americans can sign up for at different times; it is not one single service. Medicare, on average, covers about half of the health care costs for enrollees, with the difference being paid out of pocket, by individual or group/employer health insurance, or through supplemental Medigap insurance.

Note

Medicare requires you to sign up during a seven-month initial enrollment period, which starts three months before you turn 65 and ends three months after you turn 65. You can also sign up during the general enrollment period for Medicare, which runs from January 1 through March 31 of each year. *Be sure to note both enrollment periods in your financial calendar on page 216.*

As Medicare Part B does require you to pay premiums, you can elect to apply for only Medicare Part A. However, if you don't enroll in Medicare Part B during your initial enrollment period, you may have to pay a late enrollment penalty for as long as you have Medicare Part B. The exception is if you qualify for a special enrollment period. If you are age 65 or older, you or your spouse are still working, and you are covered under a group health plan based on that current employment, you may not need to apply for Medicare medical insurance (Part B) at age 65. You may qualify for a "Special Enrollment Period" (SEP) that will let you sign up for Part B.

Here is an overview of Medicare options that are important to know when organizing your financial life so you'll know what coverage you have:

1. **Original Medicare** is coverage managed by the federal government (offered through the Social Security Administration).

2. **Medicare Part A (hospital insurance).** This covers services and supplies deemed medically necessary, such as lab tests, surgery, inpatient hospital stays, skilled nursing facilities, hospice care, some home health care, and certain medical equipment (wheelchairs and walkers). This is the part funded by your payroll taxes, and so for most people there will be no further premiums to pay. Medicare Part A has a deductible and various levels of coinsurance.

3. **Medicare Part B (medical insurance).** This covers services and supplies needed to diagnose or treat your medical condition. Covered services include those that prevent illnesses, such as the flu, or diagnostic tests to detect an illness at an early stage. Also covered are services such as an annual wellness check, clinical research, ambulance services, durable medical equipment, mental health services (inpatient, outpatient, and hospitalization), getting a second opinion, and limited outpatient prescription drug costs. Medicare Part B requires a premium.

4. **Medicare Part C (Medicare Advantage plans).** These plans are offered by private insurance companies. They will cover your Medicare Parts A and B and usually offer a drug plan as well. All Medicare Advantage plans cover you for emergency and urgently needed care. Some also offer vision, hearing, dental, and/or health and wellness programs. The plans can choose to cover the costs of services that aren't medically necessary under Medicare. It's important to understand all coverage, limitations, and out-of-pocket costs.

   Medicare Advantage plans must cover everything that traditional Medicare does; however, the out-of-pocket costs can be higher than those for Medicare and Medigap policies combined. There are co-payments for provider visits, hospital care, prescription drugs, and other care. Medicare Advantage plans must limit your out-of-pocket expense to a set amount each year. Some plans have lower out-of-pocket costs, which is one distinction among plans.

5. **Medicare Part D (prescription drug coverage).** An add-on coverage to Medicare, this is offered by insurance companies and other private providers. Some Medicare Advantage plans offer prescription drug coverage as part of their services. If you do not enroll in a drug plan once you are eligible and no longer have creditable coverage, you will be subject to steep and permanent financial penalties if you choose to enroll later. Medicare Part D requires a premium.

6. **Medicare Supplements (Medigap)—Parts F, G, K, L, M, and N.** Medicare Supplement Insurance (Medigap) policies are sold by private health insurance companies and can help pay some of the health care costs that Original Medicare doesn't cover, like co-payments, coinsurance, and deductibles. Some Medigap policies also offer coverage for services that Original Medicare doesn't cover, like medical care when you travel outside the US. If you have Original Medicare and you buy a Medigap policy, Medicare will pay its share of the Medicare-approved amount for covered health care costs. Then your Medigap policy pays its share.

Please reference the table below to assist you in gathering details about your total Medicare coverage.

Medigap Benefits	Medigap Plans									
	A	B	C	D	F*	G	K	L	M	N
Part A coinsurance and hospital costs up to an additional 365 days after Medicare benefits are used up	Yes	Yes	Yes	Yes	Yes	Yes	Yes	Yes	Yes	Yes
Part B coinsurance or co-payment	Yes	Yes	Yes	Yes	Yes	Yes	50%	75%	Yes	Yes***
Blood (first 3 pints)	Yes	Yes	Yes	Yes	Yes	Yes	50%	75%	Yes	Yes
Part A hospice care coinsurance or co-payment	Yes	Yes	Yes	Yes	Yes	Yes	50%	75%	Yes	Yes
Skilled nursing facility care coinsurance	No	No	Yes	Yes	Yes	Yes	50%	75%	Yes	Yes
Part A deductible	No		Yes	Yes	Yes	Yes	50%	75%	50%	Yes
Part B deductible	No	No	Yes	No	Yes	No	No	No	No	No
Part B excess charge	No	No	No	No	Yes	Yes	No	No	No	No
Foreign travel exchange (up to plan limits)	No	No	8%	80%	80%	80%	No	No	80%	80%
Out-of-pocket limit**	N/A	N/A	N/A	N/A	N/A	N/A	$5,120 (2017)	$2,560 (2017)	N/A	N/A

- The Medigap policy covers coinsurance only after you've paid the deductible (unless the Medigap policy also pays the deductible).
  - Yes = the plan covers 100 percent of this benefit
  - No = the policy doesn't cover that benefit
  - % = the plan covers that percentage of this benefit
  - N/A = not applicable

Continued on next page . . .

*Plan F also offers a high-deductible plan. If you choose this option, you must pay for Medicare-coveredcosts up to the deductible amount of $2,180 in 2016 ($2,200 in 2017) before your Medigap plan pays anything.

**After you meet your out-of-pocket yearly limit and your yearly Part B deductible, the Medigap plan pays 100 percent of covered services for the rest of the calendar year.

***Plan N pays 100 percent of the Part B coinsurance, except for a co-payment of up to $20 for some office visits and up to a $50 co-payment for emergency room visits that don't result in inpatient admission.

- If you live in Massachusetts, Minnesota, or Wisconsin, Medigap policies are standardized in a different way:
  - Massachusetts residents (learn more: https://www.medicare.gov/supplement -other-insurance/compare-medigap/massachusetts/medigap-massachusetts.html)
  - Minnesota residents (learn more: https://www.medicare.gov/supplement-other -insurance/compare-medigap/minnesota/medigap-minnesota.html)
  - Wisconsin residents (learn more: https://www.medicare.gov/supplement-other -insurance/compare-medigap/wisconsin/medigap-wisconsin.html)
- Find a Medigap policy here: https://www.medicare.gov/find-a-plan/questions/medigap -home.aspx

In **Table 81**, add information about your health insurance (including Medicare), dental insurance, and vision insurance as applicable. This information can be located on your summary of benefits and coverage provided by your employer or by the insurance company and/or exchange if you have individual health insurance.

Table 81: Health Insurance

	Health Insurance Individual, Group, Medicare (original), Medicare Advantage and Short-Term	Medicare Supplement	Dental Insurance	Vision Insurance
Insurance company name				
Policy or certificate number				
Type of plan (individual, employer, group, association, short-term)				
Name of employer, group, or association				
Issue date				
As of date				
Renewal date*				
Premiums* (and frequency)				

	Health Insurance Individual, Group, Medicare (original), Medicare Advantage and Short-Term	Medicare Supplement	Dental Insurance	Vision Insurance
Network type (HMO, PPO, POS, or fee for service)				
Name of exchange (for individual ACA coverage)				
If ACA plan, note tier level (bronze, gold, silver, platinum, cata- strophic care)				
If ACA, note any premium assistance				
How bills are received (mail or email)				
How premiums are paid (check, direct deposit, other)				
Agent name and contact info				
Policy and documents location*				
Website and log-in credentials				
Notes:				

*NEXT STEPS

From the table above, add the premiums to health care costs worksheet below. Add the policy expiration date to your financial calendar (page 216). Your insurance policy can be stored with your important documents, and your most recent summary of coverage and benefits should go in the insurance section of your GET READY! binder.

Note

Explanation of benefits (EOBs) are provided by your insurance company and contain the date of service, medical provider name, medical service received, amount your insurance company was charged by your provider, amount your insurance will cover, and what you will owe. It also includes deductibles and co-payments (coinsurance). It is not a bill. However, you should review to ensure accuracy. EOBs can also be used if you have a flexible spending account or health care savings account (see page 101).

The worksheet that follows will help you determine your true total annual health insurance cost. Please complete using information from **Table 81** (page 152) along with any summary of costs and benefits and an estimate of your average medical services usage.

Health Care Costs Worksheet			
Health Insurance			
Annual premium (from table 81)	Multiply cost per month/pay period by 12 months or number of pay periods in a year		$____ per month/pay period X 12 or ____ (# of) = $____
Estimate your co-pays and/or coinsurance	Primary care visits		$____ per visit x ____ visits = ____
	Specialist visits		$____ per visit x ____ visits = ____
	Urgent care visits		$____ per visit x ____ visits = ____
	Emergency room visits		$____ per visit x ____ visits = ____
Total estimated co-pays/coinsurance			$____
Prescription drug costs		Covered prescription costs	$____ per Rx x ____ initial refills = ____
	Non-covered prescription costs	$____ per Rx x ____ initial refills = ____	
Total estimated prescription costs			$____
Deductibles		Primary care	$____
	Specialty care	$____	
	Urgent care	$____	
	Hospital care	$____	
	Prescriptions (covered)	$____	
Total deductibles			$____
Out-of-pocket health care costs (including over-the-counter medications)			$____
Total estimated yearly health care costs (add premium, total co-pay/ coinsurance, deductibles, and out-of-pocket costs)			$____
Tax credits (ACA marketplace plans)			$____
Discounts (ACA marketplace plans)			$____
Net estimated annual health care costs (subtract credits and discounts from yearly health care costs)*			$____

Health Care Costs Worksheet		
Dental insurance	Premium	$_____
Deductible $_____		
Co-pay $_____ per visit x _____ visits = _____		
Out-of-pocket $_____		
Dental insurance subtotal $_____		
Vision insurance	Premium	$_____
Deductible $_____		
Co-pay $_____ per visit x _____ visits = _____		
Out-of-pocket $_____		
Vision insurance subtotal $_____		
Total estimated health care costs (including vision and dental)*		$_____

*NEXT STEPS

From the table above, add the total health care costs to the expenses section of your cash flow statement on page 193.

Homeowners and Renters Insurance

If you own a home, you almost certainly will have homeowners insurance. Homeowners insurance is usually required by lenders. Without homeowners insurance, in the event of a disaster, your home would have little if any value. Homeowners insurance pays claims for damages to your home and garage and for loss of furniture and other personal property due to damage or theft (both at home and away from home). Renters insurance is generally less expensive than homeowners insurance, and it protects the things you own while also providing some liability coverage. If you are renting, your landlord's insurance coverage will not cover your possessions (contents of your rental) in case of a fire, burglary, or other claim event, so it is important to have this extra coverage.

Note

On a homeowners and renters insurance policy, the key is to know what exactly is covered. Usually, the property and its contents are covered for the named perils. If it is an all-risk policy, every event is covered except for listed exclusions. Here's what is usually covered under a homeowners or renters insurance policy:

- **Structure of the home.** Also known as dwelling coverage, this insures the physical structure such as walls and roof.
- **Personal belongings** such as furniture and other personal property that may be damaged or stolen, both at home and away.
- **Liability for bodily injury and property damage** that you may cause to others through negligence, and for accidents that happen in and around your home, as well as away from home, if you are responsible.
- **Comprehensive personal liability.** For accidents that happen in and around your home, as well as away from home (if you are responsible).
- **Loss of use coverage.** Covers living expenses that you incur if your home is deemed uninhabitable as the result of a covered peril.
- **Additional living expenses (referred to as ALE).** If you have to leave your home because of an insured disaster. ALE is more restrictive than loss of use coverage, above.
- **Pays for any injuries occurring in and around your home to anyone other than you or your family.** Medical payments coverage also pays claims for injuries outside your home caused by you, a family member living with you, or your pet.
- **Separate structures on your property** such as barns, work sheds, fencing, and garage. Be sure to calculate the replacement cost.
- **Limited coverage.** Provides limited coverage for money, gold, jewelry, and stamp and coin collections.
- **Personal property.** Covers personal property in storage.

Tip

Ask about exclusions. Many property policies on the market today exclude (will not pay for) certain types of damage. Ask the insurer, agent, or broker exactly what causes of loss and what items are *not* covered. If you want full coverage, make that clear to the insurance company in writing. Ask whether the policy excludes or limits coverage for damage due to water, earthquakes, earth movement, mold, construction defects, or other common perils. Keep good notes in a safe place.

You may be able to purchase coverage to protect you against a flood, hurricane, or earthquake loss through an endorsement. For flood insurance, you can also purchase coverage through the National Flood Insurance Program (http://www.floodsmart.gov). In California, you can buy earthquake insurance through the California Earthquake Authority (www.earthquakeauthority.com).

On the facing page, you can add details about homeowners and renters insurance and related coverages such as flood or earthquake insurance to **Table 82**. You can find the information in the declarations page that comes with your policy renewals or with the original policy.

Table 82: Homeowners and Renters Insurance

	Homeowners	Renters
Type of coverage (homeowners, earthquake, flood, or other)		
Property insured		
Insurance company name		
Insured name(s)		
Policy number		
Policy period* (issue date and expiration date)		
As of date		
Dwelling coverage limit (and extension)		
Personal property limit		
Loss of use limit		
Deductibles (for dwelling, personal property, and loss of use)		
Personal liability		
Damage to property of others		
Medical payments to others		
Building code upgrade coverage		
Premium* (and frequency)		
Premium last paid		
Policy last reviewed		
How bills are received		
How premiums are paid		
Forms, options, and endorsements		
Exclusions		
Discounts (list all)		
Agent name and contact info		
Website and log-in credentials		
Policy and documents location*		
Notes:		

Continued on next page . . .

*NEXT STEPS

From the table above, add the premiums to the expenses section of your cash flow statement on page 193. Add the policy expiration date to your financial calendar (page 216). Your insurance policy can be stored with your important documents, and your declaration (data) pages (or copies) should go in the insurance section of your GET READY! binder.

Tip

Consider the following when reviewing your homeowners insurance:

- **Consider a higher deductible.** Increasing your deductible will lower your premium.
- **Ask your insurance agent about discounts**. You may be able to get a lower premium if your home has safety features like dead-bolt locks, smoke detectors, an alarm system, storm shutters, or fire-retardant roofing material. Persons over 55 years of age or long-term customers may also be offered discounts.
- **Insure your house, *not* the land under it.** After a disaster, the land is still there. If you do not subtract the value of the land when deciding how much homeowners insurance to buy, you will pay more than you should.
- **Get replacement coverage, not an "actual cash value" policy.** Make certain you purchase enough coverage to replace what is insured. This will give you the money to rebuild your home and replace its contents. An "actual cash value" policy is cheaper but pays only what your property is worth at the time of loss—your cost minus depreciation for age and wear.
- **Ask about any special coverage you might need.** You may have to pay extra for certain types of special property such computers, cameras, jewelry, art, antiques, musical instruments, and stamp collections. Home contents are usually reimbursed only up to 50 percent of the home's insured value, unless listed separately.

Life Insurance

The purpose of life insurance is to replace income for someone who is dependent upon the insured's income. The type of life insurance you need depends on the length of time for which you need it. Most people have a set period of time for which they need life insurance—perhaps 30 years to protect a mortgage, 18 years to provide for a child, etc. As their assets grow (retirement accounts, etc.), their need for life insurance will decline.

Note

There are two main types of life insurance:

- **Term insurance**: Pays a death benefit when someone dies. Provides coverage for a limited time period and does not accrue a cash value.

- **Permanent life insurance**: This includes whole life, universal life, variable life, guaranteed, universal life, and indexed life. Policy will have a death benefit, can be continued for a longer period of time (can go up to age 125), has a planned level premium, and may accumulate a cash value.

Tip

It's important to note that you may be able to save if you switch to an annual premium. Insurance companies charge a fee if you pay any way other than annually. Check your policy for payment options, as this fee can be quite high.

Tip

A spouse/domestic partner who does not have earnings (or has lower earnings) still contributes economic value and may need life insurance too. Also, do not forget to name a contingent beneficiary. If a contingent beneficiary is not named, the life insurance proceeds become part of the insured's estate.

In **Table 83**, enter details about your life insurance coverage, as applicable. Be sure to include information about any group life insurance, which you will find in your annual enrollment confirmation. Information on individual life insurance policies can be found on the policy data pages or, if provided, the most recent annual report.

Table 83: Life Insurance

	Policy 1	Policy 2
Insurance company name		
Policy number (or certificate)		
Individual, employer, or group (add name of group or employer)		
Insured name		
Policy owner name		
Beneficiary names (primary and contingent/secondary)		
Type (term, whole, universal, other)		
Issue date		
As of date		
Death benefit		

Continued on next page . . .

		Policy 1	Policy 2
Premium (and frequency)*			
Premium last paid			
Employer coverage Amount paid by employer ($)	Benefit details (flat amount, multiple of salary)		
Term Level premium expiration date*	Guaranteed level premium period		
Cash surrender value, if applicable*			
Surrender charge period (expiry date)*			
Permanent policies: maturity date*			
Permanent policies	Date of last in force*		
	Date to order in force*		
	Based on current premium and assumptions, years policy will stay in force		
	Premium required to keep policy in force, if policy is projected to lapse before maturity date		
For cash value policies, note dividend rate, interest rate, or hypothetical return rate, as applicable			
Indexed policies: cap rate and participation rate			
Policy loan balance*			
Policy loan annual interest payment and percentage			
Conversion or exchange provision and expiry date*			
Riders			
Ratings and/or exclusions			
How bills are received (mail, email)			
How premiums are paid (check, online)			
Location of policy and documents			
Website and log-in credentials			
Agent name and contact info			
Notes:			

Note

The premium for the first $50,000 of group term life insurance is income tax free. Premiums for additional amounts of group life insurance are subject to income tax.

Tip

You should request permanent insurance in-force illustrations every two to three years. To begin the monitoring process, get in touch with your life insurance carrier and request a current in-force illustration. You can download a sample in-force illustration request letter at www.tonysteuer.com /resources.

An in-force illustration projects future performance of a life insurance policy using current values rather than the projections at the time of the policy issue. Permanent life insurance policies are made up of various components that impact policy performance, including earnings (interest rates, dividends, and so on), mortality costs, cost of insurance charges, and expense charges. In-force illustrations are critical and the ONLY WAY to find out if your life insurance policy is performing as expected.

An in-force illustration will help you answer the following questions:

- Is the policy fully funded? In other words, will it continue to maturity (maximum age) with current premiums based on current assumptions?
- If the policy is not fully funded, what is the premium required to fund the policy to maturity, based on current assumptions?
- Is the policy overfunded? Have you paid in more than required?
- Can you terminate premiums and still have the policy continue to maturity based on current assumptions?

If your policy is not performing as expected, it can be due to one or more of the following: lower than expected earnings (interest rate, dividends, etc.), higher than expected mortality costs or cost of insurance, and/or higher than projected expense charges. For more information, read "Why Would My Life Insurance Policy Underperform" at www.tonysteuer.com/resources.

Long-Term Care Insurance

Long-term care insurance (LTCI) provides coverage to pay the costs of long term care services that are not covered by Medicare or Medicare supplements such as nursing homes, in-home care, and skilled nursing facilities. Medicare only pays for skilled care in a nursing facility for a short period (up to 100 days) and only if the patient meets all of Medicare's requirements for receiving daily skilled care. Medicare does not cover long-term custodial care or in-home care.

Every LTCI policy has certain core definitions and parameters that can differ from company to company. LTCI policies allow you to customize the various components to fit your needs and budget.

In **Table 84**, fill in the details regarding your long-term care insurance policy. This information can be found in your policy (or if you have it, the outline of coverage).

Table 84: Long-Term Care Insurance

	Long-Term Care Insurance
Insurance company name	
Individual or group (if group, add name)	
Policy number	
Issue date	
Values, as of date	

Initial monthly or daily benefit:
    home care
    facility care	

Current monthly or daily benefit:
    home care
    facility care	

Benefit period	
Elimination period (waiting period)—note details about differences by type of care	
Current total benefit pool (multiply monthly or daily benefit by benefit period)	
Inflation rider: type and percentage	
Benefit type (fixed daily benefit, indemnity/cash benefit, or reimbursement benefit)	
Non-forfeiture benefit	
Shared care benefit (yes/no)	
Premium (and frequency)*	

	Long-Term Care Insurance
Premium last paid	
As of date	
How bills are received	
How premiums are paid	
Discounts	
Riders	
Ratings and/or exclusions	
Agent name and contact info	
Location of policy and documents*	
Website address and log-in credentials	
Notes:	

*NEXT STEPS

From the table above, enter the premiums in the expenses section on your cash flow statement (page 193). Your insurance policy can be stored with your important documents. Then add a recent statement of values or outline of coverage to your GET READY! binder in the insurance section.

Tip

Some LTCI policies are facing continued premium increases. Consider the following options when you receive a notice of a premium increase:

- Do nothing. Can you afford this new premium? Are the benefits that you will receive still worth the premium? If so, keep everything as is and pay the new premium.

- Adjust different components of the policy to reduce the premium. Ask yourself if you can make any of the following changes to the policy and still have the coverage remain worthwhile to you:

  - Reduce the daily benefit amount
  - Increase the waiting period
  - Shorten the benefit period
  - Change your inflation rider—if you have a compound inflation rider, can you change it to a simple inflation rider? Can you reduce the inflation rider percentage (for example, from 5 percent to 4 percent)?
  - Change/remove other riders

- If your policy has a contingent, non-forfeiture benefit, consider taking it if you cannot afford the premiums (this would provide a paid-up, reduced pool of benefits).
- Cancel the policy.

Annuities

An annuity is a contract between you and an insurance company that requires the insurer to make payments to you, either immediately or in the future. You buy an annuity by making either a single payment or a series of payments. Similarly, your payout may come either as one lump-sum payment or as a series of payments over time.

Annuities are helpful if you have a specific need that cannot be fulfilled through another investment product. The most common reason to use annuities is for periodic payments for a specified amount of time (this can be for the rest of your life, or the life of your spouse or another person, or for a set number of years). Annuities are a good solution for someone who does not control their spending and whose spending erodes their savings. Purchasing an annuity will "lock" up your money and allow you to receive a guaranteed income. When you compare an annuity to other investments, you will find higher fees, and you will pay surrender charges that over the long run will cost you more and result in lower accumulated funds.

There are three basic types of annuities:

- **Fixed annuity:** The insurance company promises you a minimum rate of interest and a fixed amount of periodic payments. State insurance commissioners regulate fixed annuities. Please check with your state's Department of Insurance (DOI) website (links to each state's DOI can be found at www.naic.org) about the risks and benefits of fixed annuities and to confirm that your insurance broker is registered to sell insurance in your state.

- **Variable annuity:** The insurance company allows you to direct your annuity payments to different investment options (usually mutual funds). Your payout will vary depending on how much you put in, the rate of return on your investments, and expenses. The SEC regulates variable annuities. Variable annuities include several charges, such as mortality and expense risk charges, administrative fees, underlying fund expenses along with penalties, surrender charges, and partial withdrawal limitations.

- **Indexed annuity:** This annuity combines features of securities and insurance products. The insurance company credits you with a return that is based on a stock market index, such as the Standard & Poor's 500 Index. State insurance commissioners regulate indexed annuities. Indexed annuities have several limitations and fees, including administrative fees, miscellaneous fees and charges for other features, surrender charges, partial withdrawal limitations, interest (earnings) cap, and participation rate.

It's also important for your records to document if your annuity is in the accumulation phase or the payout phase.

- **Accumulation phase:** When your payments are made into the annuity and accumulate based on the type of annuity.

- **Payout phase:** When you receive your payments back, along with any investment income and gains. You may take the payout in one lump-sum payment, or you may choose to receive a regular stream of payments, generally monthly.

In **Table 85,** you can add details about annuities that you own. You can find this information either in your annual statements or in your original contracts.

Table 85: Annuities

	Annuity 1	Annuity 2
Insurance company name (contact info)		
Contract #		
Issue date (contract date)		
Type of annuity (single premium or flexible premium)		
Annuity phase (accumulation or payout)		
Owner		
Annuitant(s) (person(s) who will receive benefit)		
Beneficiary		
Single premium paid in		
Flexible premium amount and frequency*		
Cost basis (sum of premiums paid—include roll-over cost basis)		
Surrender charge period (expiry date)*		
Withdrawal limit		
As of date		
Cash accumulation method (fixed, indexed, variable, or other)		
If fixed, list interest rate		

Continued on next page . . .

	Annuity 1	Annuity 2
If indexed, list interest rate cap and participation rate		
If variable or indexed, list sub-accounts		
If applicable, list interest rate bonus (amount and terms)		
Current total account value		
Current total surrender value*		
Current annuitization value (if different)		
If you are in the payout phase, list the option (life, certain period, joint with certain period, other)		
Monthly benefit*		
Exclusion ratio for payouts		
Survivor benefit (if yes, list percentage or choices)		
Payouts (received via check or direct deposit—note name of bank account)		
Riders		
Agent name & contact info		
Website and log-in credentials		
Location of documents*		
Notes (such as plans to annuitize):		

*NEXT STEPS

From the table above, enter any payments that you are receiving as income on your cash flow statement (page 193). Then, enter any premiums you are paying as an expense onto your cash flow statement. Add the surrender period expiration date to your financial calendar (page 216). Store your annuity contracts with your secure documents. Then add your most recent annuity statement into your GET READY! binder in the insurance section.

Miscellaneous Insurance Policies

There are many other types of insurance policies. Following are some of the more common types of insurance that you might have:

- **Accidental death and dismemberment:** A type of coverage that pays benefits, sometimes including reimbursement for loss of income, in case of sickness, accidental injury, or accidental death.

- **Critical illness insurance:** Provides a lump-sum cash payment if the policyholder is diagnosed with one of the critical illnesses listed in the insurance policy.

- **Errors and omissions insurance (E&O):** Business liability insurance for professionals such as insurance agents, real estate agents and brokers, architects, third-party administrators (TPAs), and other business professionals.

- **Identity theft insurance:** Provides reimbursement to crime victims for the cost of restoring their identity and repairing credit reports. Some companies now include this as part of their homeowners insurance policy; others sell it as a stand-alone policy. Ask your homeowner policy company for information.

- **Pet insurance:** This coverage insures pets against accidents and illnesses; some companies also cover routine/wellness care and burial/cremation services.

- **Travel insurance:** This is insurance coverage taken by those who travel abroad, which covers certain losses such as medical expenses, loss of personal belongings, travel delay, and personal liabilities.

- **Personal umbrella policies:** You can add personal liability with a stand-alone "umbrella" policy. This is a cost-effective way to increase your liability coverage by $1 million or more, in case you are at fault in an accident or someone is injured on your property. It supplements the insurance you already have for home, auto, and other personal property.

In **Table 86**, add any details about other insurance policies that you have. This information can usually be found on your policy declaration pages.

Table 86: Miscellaneous Insurance Policies

Type of coverage		
Insurance company name		
Insured name(s)		
Policy number		
Policy period (issue date and expiration date)*		
Values, as of date		

Continued on next page . . .

Coverage limits (or benefits)		
Premium (and frequency)*		
Premium last paid		
As of date		
How bills are received		
How premiums are paid		
Forms, options, and endorsements		
Exclusions		
Discounts (list all)		
Agent name and contact info		
Website and log-in credentials		
Policy and documents location*		
Notes:		

*NEXT STEPS

From the table above, add the premiums to the expenses section of your cash flow statement on page 193. Add policy expiration dates to your financial calendar (page 216). Your insurance policy can be stored with your important documents, and your declaration (data) pages (or copies) should go in the insurance section of your GET READY! binder.

END-OF-CHAPTER CHECK-IN

Did this chapter help you GET READY!? In the following table, assess your level of financial preparedness by checking the appropriate status box for all the topics in this chapter.

	In Progress	Completed	Not Applicable
Auto insurance			
Disability insurance			
Health insurance			

	In Progress	Completed	Not Applicable
Homeowners and renters insurance			
Life insurance			
Long-term care insurance			
Annuities			
Other insurance coverage			

 PRINT FORMS

To print these forms, visit my website at www.tonysteuer.com/resources.

NOTES

CHAPTER 9

Estate Planning

Plans are nothing; planning is everything.
—Dwight D. Eisenhower

It's great to have a plan, but if you don't let others know about your plan, then it's pretty much useless. When planning a wilderness trip, for example, a common practice in strategizing about a possible emergency is to tell someone who is not going on the trip your itinerary and an estimated return date. That way if you don't check in by the return date, rescuers will have a general idea of where to start a search.

Estate planning and final arrangements work the same way. If you don't let anyone know your wishes, and put those wishes in writing, those you leave behind will at best be guessing about how to proceed. Speaking with your loved ones and putting the information in writing is the difference between having a plan and actually planning.

Failing to plan your estate is planning to fail. It's as simple as that. Estate planning is an area where you cannot fix mistakes when the plan goes into effect (after you pass away), so it is strongly recommended that you work with a qualified estate planning attorney who will help you execute your plan. You can find an estate planning attorney by asking for referrals from people you know or by visiting the National Association of Estate Planners and Councils website (www.naepc.org) to find an attorney near you.

If there is any person or organization that you would like to continue to support if you are disabled or die, then you must take the time to come up with an appropriate plan to do so. If you do not make such a plan, there are laws that will dictate how your affairs are handled and how your finances are distributed. You spend your lifetime building your financial house, so I encourage you to take the time to ensure your legacy is distributed according to your own wishes rather than the state's.

 GET READY!: ESTATE PLANNING AND FINAL ARRANGEMENTS

In this chapter, we're going to take a look at your estate planning and final arrangements wishes. While organizing this part of the planner, you will learn about—

OWNERSHIP OF PROPERTY

There are multiple ways to own property. This is referred to as how you hold title. Following are the different forms of ownership:

- **Sole (or separate) property:** Property is held in your name only.
- **Community property:** Property is held equally (in community) by husband and wife and has accumulated during marriage (except through inheritance or gift). Community property laws are in effect in nine states: Arizona, California, Idaho, Louisiana, Nevada, New Mexico, Texas, Washington, and Wisconsin.
- **Community property with rights of survivorship:** Property is held equally (in community) by husband and wife and has accumulated during marriage (except through inheritance or gift). If one person dies, his or her share automatically transfers to the survivor.
- **Joint tenancy with rights of survivorship:** This is a method of ownership in which two or more persons can hold equal or unequal percentages in real estate, financial investments, or personal property. If one person dies, his or her share automatically transfers to the survivor(s), even if a will specifies otherwise.
- **Tenancy by the entirety:** This is ownership of property by a husband and wife together that includes a right of survivorship. Neither spouse can encumber or dispose of the property without the other's permission. This way of holding title is not recognized in all states.
- **Tenant-in-common:** This pertains to two or more holders of equal or unequal shares of property, which carries no rights of survivorship.
- **Trust:** A trust is an arrangement set up by a legal agreement designed to manage and control certain assets, usually held by one person or persons for the benefit of others.

1. **Power(s) of attorney (POA) and advanced directives.** You will be making a list of all of your POAs and advanced directives. You'll also record information on the details.

2. **Final arrangements.** You'll be able to summarize all of your wishes for final arrangements, including a letter of intent, organ donation, burial and cremation preference, and funeral and celebration of life ceremonies.

3. **Wills and trusts.** You also will be documenting wills and trusts that you have in place along with their major components.

4. **Digital estate planning.** And you'll have an opportunity to consider how your digital life and assets will be handled after your death.

5. **Pet estate planning.** In this section, you'll be able to add details of any plans that you've made for your pets' continued care after your passing.

You should review your estate plan and final arrangements every two or three years or when you have an important life event such as change in marital status, birth of a child (or grandchild), retirement, or death of an heir or someone with a role in administering your estate such as a guardian, trustee, or executor.

Power of Attorney

A power of attorney (POA) is someone you appoint to make legal and financial decisions on your behalf in case you are no longer able to do so. In the event that you become incapacitated, this will allow your agent to be able to act on your behalf. A POA is revocable by you (as principal) at any time (you must be deemed to be physically able and/or mentally competent) or upon death. Usually spouses will set up reciprocal powers of attorney. You should consult with a qualified attorney to set this up as part of your estate planning. It is important to do this early on, because if there is no POA, there is no one who can legally handle your financial affairs, and it will be up to a court to decide if you are mentally competent and what happens to your financial affairs.

Note

There are two types of power of attorney:

- **Durable**: Durable powers of attorney remain effective after you are incapacitated and are unable to manage your own affairs. All powers granted will terminate upon your death.

- **Non-durable:** Non-durable powers of attorney become invalid in the event that you become incapacitated. If these are terminated, you should destroy the documents, so they are not mistakenly used.

In **Table 87**, you can add the basic details of any powers of attorney that you have. This information can be found in your POA documents. This is also a good time to consider obtaining a POA if you do not currently have one.

BENEFICIARIES

A beneficiary is the designated person(s) or entity, such as a trust, that will receive an asset when you pass away. It is important to name a beneficiary so that assets can pass directly to that person(s) or entity without going through a will, probate, or intestacy laws. A contingent beneficiary is designated in case the primary beneficiary(ies) passes away before you do and you don't have a chance to update your beneficiary designations. Most investment accounts, including retirement plans and insurance policies, allow you to name a beneficiary. Certain assets are mandated by state and federal laws to have your spouse as primary beneficiary unless they provide a written waiver.

Table 87: Power of Attorney

Type of POA	Durable	Non-durable
Document full title		
Date prepared		
Date effective (immediately, upon incapacity, or other)		
Termination date		
Name of agent (for your POA)		
Date you advised your agent		
Date you gave your agent a copy of the document		
Alternate (contact info)		
Powers		

Continued on next page . . .

Type of POA	Durable	Non-durable
Prepared by (name, title, contact information)		
Location of original document*		
Location of copies*		
Notes		

*NEXT STEPS

Keep the original POA with your secure documents. Add a copy of your POA to the estate planning section of your GET READY! binder. You may also give your agent a copy of the POA.

Tip

You should meet with your POA every two to three years or when you've had a major life event, so that you can go over your goals and expectations regarding your finances and legal matters.

Health Care Directives/Advanced Directive/Health Care Power of Attorney

An advance directive allows you to specify what types of treatments you want and don't want at the end of your life. It also allows you to designate another person (usually your spouse or other family member) to communicate your specified health care decisions in the event of your incapacitation. It's important to choose someone you trust. This person should also understand your views and be able to communicate them clearly, as their decisions will impact your life. You should also name a back-up agent in the event your primary agent is not available or unable to fulfill their duties.

This is a legal document and usually can be accomplished by completing your state's advance directive forms. In some states, a living will and the health care proxy/power of attorney can be combined into one form; in other states, they must be separate forms. You must also have two witnesses over the age of 18 sign the form while having the form notarized (if required).

If you have a health care directive, you can note the main components in **Table 88**.

Table 88: Health Care Directives/Advanced Directive/ Health Care Power of Attorney

Full title of document	
Date prepared	
Date effective (immediately, upon my incapacity, or other)	
Health care agent (proxy) name (contact info)	
Alternate (contact info)	
Powers	
Do not resuscitate (DNR) order included?	
Types of life-support treatment that you want and don't want	
Prepared by (name, title, contact information)	
Location of original document*	
Location of copies (agent, physician, hospital, other)	
Notes:	

*NEXT STEPS

Keep the original advanced health care directive with your secure documents. Add a copy of your directive to the estate planning section of your GET READY! binder. Be sure that your primary health care providers also have a copy.

 Note

It is important to discuss your health care proxy with your family or other trusted advisor or friend so they can be familiar with your wishes; let them know you have an advanced health care directive. If nobody knows it exists, it can't be used.

Final Arrangements

Final arrangements consist of what your wishes are for your remains and memorial services. While death is not easy to think about, it is harder still for those who are left behind who may be left guessing as to what you would have liked. While how you live your life will always be part of your history, you can also have a say in how you are remembered. So, make the time now to plan your final arrangements so that your loved ones can be left with the peace of mind that your final wishes are being honored.

Letter of Intent/Letter of Instruction

A letter of intent is a document left to your executor or beneficiary. The purpose is to define what you want done with a particular asset after your death or incapacitation. Some letters of intent also provide funeral details or other special requests.

While a letter of intent may not be valid in the eyes of the law, it helps inform a probate judge of your intentions and may help in the distribution of your assets if the will is deemed invalid for some reason.

If you have written a letter of intent, please note the following:

Location:* _____

Date last updated: _____

Whom you have told: _____

---

*NEXT STEPS _____

Store the original letter of intent with your secure documents. Add a copy to the estate planning section of your GET READY! binder.

Donation of Organs or Body

If you have agreed to be an organ donor or donor of your full body, please complete **Table 89**.

Table 89: Donation of Organs or Body

Location of uniform donor card (if you have one) or driver's license	
Name of organ donation registry	
Organ or tissues specified for donation	
If donating your body, which medical school or research organization have you made pre-arrangements with	

Name of preferred medical school or research organization (if none pre-arranged)	
Location of documents*	
Notes and special instructions:	

*NEXT STEPS

Store a copy of any donor card or other documents in the estate planning section of your GET READY! binder.

Note

Here are some common organs that are donated: heart, kidneys, liver, lungs, and pancreas. The following common tissues are also donated: blood vessels, bone, cartilage, corneas, heart valves, inner ear, intestines, and skin.

Burial and Cremation

In the table below, add details for your preferences for burial or cremation. If you have made pre-arrangements or outlined your wishes in another document, refer to that document to complete **Table 90.**

Table 90: Burial and Cremation

Burial or cremation	
Immediate or after services	
Embalm or do not embalm	
Burial: in ground or above ground (crypt, mausoleum, other)	
Cremation: scattered (and where), in ground, to individual or location	
Casket, urn, or other (with details: material, model or design, exterior finish, cost range)	
Headstone or other marker details (description, material, design, finish)	
Epitaph or other inscription (if longer, use notes at end of chapter)	

Continued on next page . . .

Apparel details, including location	
Organization name and location	
Pre-arrangement details (including pre-payment)*	
Location of documents that contain these wishes	
Person(s) you've discussed these wishes with	
Notes:	

*NEXT STEPS

Keep your instructions and any pre-arrangement documents with your secure documents. Add copies of instructions or pre-arrangement documents to the estate planning section of your GET READY! binder.

Viewings, Visitations, and Wakes

There are many different options to consider for viewings, visitations, and wakes. In **Table 91**, you can add details on your wishes—whether you want to have a viewing, visitation, or wake.

Table 91: Viewings, Visitations, and Wakes

Type (viewing, visitation, or wake)	
Service details (religious considerations)	
Body present (yes or no)	
Casket (open or closed or not there)	
Public or private	
People to invite	
Where to find invitees contact info	
Timing (days and hours)	
Special requests	
Preferred location	

Pre-arrangement details and document location*	
Contact info for pre-arrangements	
Requests	
Notes:	

*NEXT STEPS

Keep your instructions and any pre-arrangement documents with your secure documents. Add copies of instructions or pre-arrangement documents to the estate planning section of your GET READY! binder.

Funeral and Memorial Services

When planning a funeral or memorial service, there are many aspects of the service that you can plan and personalize, including religious traditions, customs, features, readings, eulogy, music, and participants. In **Table 92**, add details for any pre-arranged services, along with any preferences.

Table 92: Funeral and Memorial Service

Type (funeral, memorial, or other)	
Service type and related contact info (religious, military, other)	
Location (funeral home, place of worship, home, other)	
Religious leader/officiant/clergy	
Speakers/readers	
Body/casket present (yes/no)	
Casket (open/closed)	
Public or private	
People to invite (location of contact info)	
Groups to notify (clubs, veteran's groups, other)	
Ushers/pallbearers	
Readings (favorite scripture, psalms, poems)	

Continued on next page . . .

Music (special hymns, music, musicians, soloists)	
Milestones to mention in eulogy	
Items to bring (photos, videos, other)	
Where flowers/donations should be sent	
Other notes about financial arrangement	
Military honor details	
Funeral program details	
Pre-arrangements (company/service and location)	
Location of documents*	
If burial after service, note details on graveside ceremony	
Notes:	

*NEXT STEPS

Keep your instructions and any pre-arrangement document with your secure documents. Add copies of instructions or pre-arrangement documents to the estate planning section of your GET READY! binder.

Celebration of Life Ceremony and Reception

If you would like a celebration of life ceremony, reception, or other gathering, please complete **Table 93** to note your wishes.

Table 93: Celebration of Life Ceremony and Reception

Type of celebration (celebration of life, reception, banquet, other)	
Details on any pre-arrangements*	
Arrangement details: place/time	
Public or private	
People to invite (names and where to find contact info)	

Location suggestion	
Food/beverage suggestions	
Music details (suggested music or playlist)	
Video details (what to include or if you have made a video)	
Photos (what to include or if you have already selected photos)	
Person you've discussed this with	
Location of any documents*	
Notes (other requests):	

*NEXT STEPS

Keep your instructions and any pre-arrangement document with your secure documents. Add copies of instructions or pre-arrangement documents to the estate planning section of your GET READY! binder.

Obituary

In **Table 94**, please note whether you have already written an obituary, or note any details that you would like to appear in your obituary, including if you would prefer to not have an obituary published.

Table 94: Obituary

Location of an existing obituary (computer file name or physical location)*	
Obituary length (short, moderate, long)	
Photograph to include (and location) (or no photo, if you prefer not to include one)	
Publications (print or online)	

Note which of the following information should be included (or not):

Full name (with nickname and/or maiden name)	
Date and location of death	
Cause of death	
Funeral or memorial service details (see Tables 90–92) (public or private)	

Continued on next page . . .

Place and date of birth	
Spouse's name	
Date and place married	
Children and grandchildren names	
Parents' names	
Education (schools/degrees)	
Military (honors/achievements/medals)	
Employment (titles/achievements)	
Affiliations (religious, cultural, civic)	
Special accomplishments	
Hobbies and interests	
Personality and character	
Donations or remembrances (to where, with website info and/or phone number)	
Flowers (yes or no—if yes, where to send)	
Pre-paid obituary details (usually with a pre-paid service package)*	
Notes and other details:	

*NEXT STEPS

Add a copy of your obituary to the estate planning section of your GET READY! binder.

Note

In the event that something should happen to you, your children will need someone to look after them if they are still minors. Therefore, it's important to name a guardian so you can choose who your children will live with and be raised by in the event of your early passing. If applicable, consider whether the guardian shares your philosophies, is financially stable, and is willing and able to take on this responsibility. If you do not designate a guardian, a court will often decide who your children will live with, which will most likely be a family member—and might not be your first choice. Courts may also rule that your child become a ward of the state. A court can also on rare occasions overrule a guardianship designation, though they will give significant consideration to a parent's wishes first.

Sometimes, a person may make an excellent guardian for your child(ren) but may not be someone you would like to have control of the money. In this event, a separate financial guardian, such as a trustee, can be responsible for the money until your child reaches the age at which you are comfortable giving them access to the money. (If you have a trust, that will usually be the age of majority, as ruled by your state.)

Note

A bequest is the legal word for a gift of personal property such as stocks, bonds, jewelry, and cash through the provisions of a will or estate plan. Bequests can be made to family, friends, institutions, or charities.

Ethical Will

An ethical will is a personal document that you create to communicate your values, experiences, and life lessons to your family. It is not a legally binding document and does not replace a last will and testament. However, by leaving your family an ethical will, you'll be leaving something meaningful behind, so members of your family can remember you and your words of wisdom. When crafting an ethical will, be casual, use your own words, and make it your own. Usually this is a work in progress rather than a finished product.

In **Table 95**, you can enter information that you have included or may wish to include in an ethical will.

Table 95: Ethical Will

Names of those who should receive your ethical will	
Family (story and important things learned from my life partner, children, dad, mom, grandparents)	
Experiences (best experience, worst experience, and lessons learned)	
Professional life and accomplishments	
Favorite memories	
Beliefs and values	
What I want others to know	
Favorites (movies, books, musicians, artists, recipes, places, restaurants, sports and teams, hobbies)	
Location of ethical will*	
Notes:	

Continued on next page . . .

Wills

Wills are legally enforceable declarations of how a person wants their property or assets to be distributed
after death. In a will a person can state their final wishes, including recommending a guardian for any
minor children and making provisions for any surviving pets. A will may also be referred to as a "Last
Will and Testament."

Note

If you die without a will, your property will be distributed under the intestacy laws of the state
where you reside. These laws dictate how your assets (property) are distributed upon your death.
This includes bank accounts, investments, retirement accounts, real estate, and everything else. If
real estate property is located in a different state, the intestacy laws of that state will apply. Your
estate will also go into probate, which can take up to nine months, and your heirs could potentially
claim more than their intended share of assets, creating a costly legal mess.

All estates go through probate, so estate planning documents will speed up the process. The
laws of intestate succession also vary greatly depending on whether you are single, married, or have
children. Generally, your assets will be distributed in split shares to your "heirs," which can include
your surviving spouse, siblings, aunts and uncles, nieces, nephews, and even distant relatives. When
there are no heirs, your entire estate will go to the state. You can find links to each state's intestate
laws here: http://estate.findlaw.com/planning-an-estate/intestate-succession-laws-by-state.html.

Note

An executor is the person who will oversee the liquidation and distribution of the decedent's assets
according to the terms of the will and pay off outstanding debts and taxes on the estate. An executor may be an attorney or financial expert or anyone the writer of the will trusts to act responsibly.
The executor may be entitled to receive a reasonable fee for their services. Fee guidelines may be
mandated by the state. In a will you can use bequests to leave assets that don't have beneficiary
designations to people or entities such as a nonprofit. You can also include instructions about your
funeral and burial wishes.

In **Table 96**, note the main details of your will for easy reference.

Table 96: Wills

Full title	
Date of the will	
Will update(s)—codicil date(s)	
Executor of will (with contact info)	
Executor alternate	
Guardian(s) of the person (with contact info)	
Alternative guardian of the person	
Guardian(s) of the property	
Alternative guardian of the property	
Beneficiaries listed	
Assets listed (Chapters 3, 4 & 5)	
Debts included (Chapter 7)	
Is there a non-contestability clause?	
Attorney who has copy of will (name, firm name, contact info)	
Prior will versions	
Will location*	
Person(s) with copies of will	
Notes:	

*NEXT STEPS

Keep the original will with your secure documents. Add a copy of your will to the estate planning section of your GET READY! binder.

Trusts

A trust (or trust fund) is a legal entity that allows a person (the grantor, donor, or settlor) to transfer assets to another person or organization (the trustee). Once the grantor establishes the trust, the trustee controls and manages the assets for the grantor or for another beneficiary—someone who will ultimately benefit from the trust. A trust carries rules and provisions that you create to dictate what happens to the assets held under the ownership of the trust. Because there are various types of trusts, you will want to decide what type best meets your objectives and ensure you follow the rules for that trust so the legal requirements continue to be met.

There are many types of trusts. The most common type is a living trust that the grantor sets up while they are still alive; this is known as an "inter vivos" trust. A trust set up after death, commonly through a will, is known as "testamentary." Trusts can be revocable, which means they can be changed, or they can be irrevocable, which means they can't be changed.

Note

Trusts are an essential part of estate planning, as they provide the following useful features:

- Provide for minor children or family members who are inexperienced or unable to handle financial matters.
- Arrange for management of personal assets, if you become unable to handle them yourself.
- Avoid probate and have assets immediately transferred to beneficiaries upon death.
- Afford privacy. Terms of a trust are private, whereas terms of a will are public.
- Protect assets from beneficiaries' creditors or legal situations.
- Donate to nonprofits.
- Avoid or reduce estate and gift taxes.

If you have set up a trust, please complete **Table 97** for up to two trusts. If you have more than two trusts, you can add any additional information in the Notes section at the end of this chapter. The information requested below can be found in your trust documents, which should include a summary page.

Table 97: Trusts

	Trust 1	Trust 2
Full name of the trust		
Date of trust (date executed)		
Is trust revocable or irrevocable?		
Trust (codicil) revision date(s)		
Grantor names (or settlor or trustor)		
Grantor (or trustors)		
Trustee names (all and addresses)		
Successor trustees		

	Trust 1	Trust 2
Trust tax ID number		
Trustee powers (acquire additional property, sell and execute deeds, to encumber, other)		
Number of trustees required to sign documents to exercise the powers of the trust (and names)		
Title to which trust assets will be taken		
Name of attorney or legal service that prepared trust		
Trust contact information		
Location of the original trust*		
Location of copies of the trust*		
Notes:		

*NEXT STEPS

Keep the original trust documents with your secure documents. Add a copy of your trust to the estate planning section of your GET READY! binder.

Digital Estate Planning

The internet and technology have created a whole new world. And with this new world has come a whole new set of considerations in our final planning. Our "digital assets"—email accounts, websites, blogs, social media accounts, internet membership sites, cloud storage, and other internet- and software-related activities—present us with a new category of estate planning known as digital estate planning.

In fact, this has become a new area of estate planning with the implementation of the Revised Uniform Fiduciary Access to Digital Assets Act (RUFADAA). This law was developed primarily by the Uniform Law Commission to provide fiduciaries (such as POA agents, executors, and trustees) with legal authorization to manage digital assets of deceased and incapacitated individuals. This act was necessary since terms of service agreements and privacy policies of social media, email account, blogs, and so on terminated when the account holder passed away and are not transferrable.

It is up to each state to enact this law. RUFADAA gives fiduciaries certain powers to manage digital assets, but it also attempts to provide some privacy protections for the "owners" of the digital assets, as well as legal protections for "custodians" (the businesses who make, store, or provide digital assets).

At the time of the writing of this book, at least 42 states have enacted laws to address access to digital accounts. You can read more about RUFADAA here:

https://www.americanbar.org/content/dam/aba/publications/real_property_trust_and_estate
_law_journal/v52/01/rpte-journal-2017-52-1-article-new-uniform-digital-assets-law-estate
-planning-and-administration-in-information-age%20.authcheckdam.pdf.

Keep in mind that these are new laws, and they can differ slightly from state to state or in their interpretation. It is important to be clear in your estate planning documents (will, trust, POA) regarding your wishes for your digital assets. For example, you can write a separate letter of instruction to specify a digital executor.

In **Table 98**, list any digital assets that would require action after you pass away. For example, Facebook can create a memorial page, while other services can be transferred to family members. For the most part, these will be social media services. In other sections you will have added the website address and log-in credentials. Here you only need to indicate the actions to be taken and by whom.

Table 98: Digital Estate Planning

	Website/Service	Action (keep active, archive, delete, other)
Digital executor name and contact information		
Email account 1		
Email account 2		
Blog 1		
Blog 2		
Website		
Dating site		
Facebook		
Google		
Instagram		
Twitter		
Snapchat		
Other		
Location of letter of instruction*		
Notes:		

Pet Estate Planning

Pets are often overlooked in estate planning, yet they are a part of the family. In **Table 99**, add details on your wishes for your pets. If you have more than two pets, you can use the Notes section at the end of this chapter.

Table 99: Pet Estate Planning

Name of pet	
Type of pet	
Is pet covered in your will or special pet trust?	
If pet trust, list name, date, and location	
Arrangements you have made for physical care of pet (name and contact info)	
Financial arrangements for the care of your pet	
Location of documents*	
Notes:	

Note

For more information on the various components of estate planning, visit the American Bar Association's website at https://www.americanbar.org/groups/real_property_trust_estate/resources/estate_planning/estate_planning_faq.html.

 **END-OF-CHAPTER CHECK-IN**

Did this chapter help you GET READY!? In the following table, assess your level of financial preparedness by checking the appropriate status box for all the topics in this chapter.

	In Progress	Completed	Not Applicable
Power(s) of attorney			
Advanced/health care directives			
Organ or body donations			
Burial and cremation			
Funeral and memorial services			
Obituary			
Ethical will			
Will (and last testament)			
Trusts			
Digital estate planning			
Pet estate planning			

 PRINT FORMS

To print these forms, visit my website at www.tonysteuer.com/resources.

NOTES

_____

_____

_____

_____

_____

_____

_____

CHAPTER 10

Evaluating Your Financial Readiness

If you are prepared, you will be confident, and will do the job.
—Tom Landry

When you go on an overnight hiking or camping trip, you plan ahead and gather your supplies for your emergency first aid kit. Before you can go on your trip, however, there is one last step—to double-check that you have everything you need. When you're out in the wilderness, emergency situations occur quickly, and you must be ready to act. When these emergencies strike, you won't have time to stock your emergency kit or spend time gathering your supplies, so you'll be glad that you have a first aid kit on hand. Instead, you need to be set and ready. Doing a review of everything you've gathered before you head out on your outdoor adventure gives you another opportunity to make sure that you haven't missed anything.

Organizing your financial first aid kit is a lot like preparing for an outdoor excursion. When it comes to your finances, you will need to bring all of your financial life into a central dashboard, so you can have a big-picture view of your life and see how all of the pieces fit together when looked at as a whole rather than as separate parts. In other words, you need to be sure you can see the proverbial forest for the trees.

In this chapter, we will do a final check of your financial first aid kit so you can be sure you are prepared. We will bring everything together through a cash flow statement, a net worth statement, a retirement tracker, and a master financial checklist. Looking at these items in context will allow you to see if there is something missing or if there is an area where you need to cut back.

 GET READY!: EVALUATING YOUR FINANCIAL READINESS

In this chapter, we're going to look at your financial life and see how all of the individual parts work together. In particular, we will visit your—

1. **Cash flow analysis and budget.** In this chapter, you will be gathering all of your income and expenses into a cash flow analysis that you can use to create a budget.

2. **Net worth statement.** Then, you'll make an inventory of your assets and liabilities.

3. **Retirement planning tracker.** After that, you'll review your retirement plans to see if they are sufficient to meet your retirement goals.

4. **Financial ratios.** You'll also be able to use the information you've gathered to help monitor your financial health.

5. **GET READY! summary.** Lastly, you'll be able to bring in all of the items from prior chapters, so you can assess your overall progress.

Gathering this data no doubt heightened your awareness of your own financial needs, choices, and issues. When it comes to managing your money, that kind of awareness is one of the real keys to success.

 Tip

You can use the information in this chapter to also help you in other areas, such as filing your taxes or applying for a loan.

Creating a Cash Flow Analysis and Budget

A cash flow analysis is important, since it will show you what your income is and what your expenses are. Understanding your cash flow is an important aspect of organizing your financial life and getting ready for the future. Documenting your income and expenses will also allow your spouse/domestic partner and/or your heirs to easily see how your money is flowing.

Your expenses should always be lower than your income so that there are additional funds that can be used to save for retirement and emergency expenses. If your expenses are higher than your income, you have two choices: increase your income or reduce your expenses.

 Note

Budgets are a subject of much debate as to whether they are truly important to a sound financial plan. There are many websites and books that are dedicated strictly to budgeting, and budgeting is even part of most financial planning software. Ultimately, using (and sticking to) a budget is up to you. Whether or not you choose to use a budget, it's important to review your cash flow at least once a year.

The following cash flow statement worksheet allows you to gauge your cash flow and integrate it into a budget. If you entered these items when you completed the earlier chapters in this book, the worksheet should be easy to complete. You can also find this information in your recent statements for each line item. All you'll need to do is make some calculations to convert your expense amounts to an annual sum. The budgeted amount and over/under columns are there if you wish to create a budget. The "over or under" column will show you where you need to consider changing either your actual amount or your budgeted amount. The more thoroughly you complete this worksheet, the more helpful it will be. You can also download this worksheet from www.tonysteuer.com/resources if you are creating a binder or need additional pages. If any of the items do not apply, simply leave them blank.

Cash Flow Statement as of Date: _____

	Actual Amount (annual)	Budgeted Amount	Over or Under Amount
INCOME			
EARNED INCOME			
Cash compensation (primary job)	$_____	$_____	$_____
Second job (side job)	$_____	$_____	$_____
Online income/sales	$_____	$_____	$_____
Royalties (copyrights, trademarks, patents, other)	$_____	$_____	$_____
Other earned income	$_____	$_____	$_____
Subtotal: Earned Income	$_____	$_____	$_____
UNEARNED INCOME/INVESTMENT INCOME			
Checking, savings accounts	$_____	$_____	$_____
Stock dividends	$_____	$_____	$_____
Treasury securities	$_____	$_____	$_____
Bond(s) annual yield	$_____	$_____	$_____
Mutual fund dividends	$_____	$_____	$_____
Exchange-traded fund dividends	$_____	$_____	$_____
Royalties (copyrights, trademarks, patents, other)	$_____	$_____	$_____
Debt and obligations owed to you—interest	$_____	$_____	$_____
Other income	$_____	$_____	$_____
Reverse mortgage payout	$_____	$_____	$_____
Annuity distributions	$_____	$_____	$_____
Other unearned income	$_____	$_____	$_____
Subtotal: Unearned Income/ Investment Income	$_____	$_____	$_____

Continued on next page . . .

	Actual Amount (annual)	Budgeted Amount	Over or Under Amount

RETIREMENT INCOME

	Actual Amount (annual)	Budgeted Amount	Over or Under Amount
IRA	$	$	$
401(k), 403(b), and 457 plan(s)	$	$	$
Pension	$	$	$
Social security	$	$	$
Other retirement income	$	$	$
Subtotal: Retirement Income	$	$	$
Total income	**$**	**$**	**$**

EXPENSES

SAVINGS AND INVESTING

	Actual Amount (annual)	Budgeted Amount	Over or Under Amount
Checking and savings account fees	$	$	$
Brokerage account fees	$	$	$
Investing fees	$	$	$
College savings account contributions	$	$	$
ABLE account contribution	$	$	$
Other savings and investing expenses	$	$	$
Flexible spending accounts	$	$	$
Subtotal: Savings and Investing	**$**	**$**	**$**

RETIREMENT SAVINGS

	Actual Amount (annual)	Budgeted Amount	Over or Under Amount
Individual retirement account (IRAs)	$	$	$
Self-employed and small business IRA(s)	$	$	$
401(k), 403(b), and 457 plan(s)	$	$	$
Other employer and group retirement plan(s)	$	$	$
Other retirement funding	$	$	$
Subtotal: Retirement Savings	**$**	**$**	**$**

	Actual Amount (annual)	Budgeted Amount	Over or Under Amount
LOANS AND DEBTS			
Loans	$	$	$
Car loan and lease payment(s)	$	$	$
Mortgage (primary residence) payment	$	$	$
Mortgage payment (HELOC and home equity)	$	$	$
Private mortgage insurance payment	$	$	$
Vacation home and time-share payment	$	$	$
Student loan payment(s)	$	$	$
Investment property payments	$	$	$
Business property loan payment(s) (commercial)	$	$	$
Personal debts and loan payment(s)	$	$	$
Credit card payment(s)	$	$	$
Debt consolidation loan payment(s)	$	$	$
Other loan payment(s)	$	$	$
Subtotal: Loans and Debts	$	$	$

UTILITY AND HOUSEHOLD EXPENSES			
Cable/satellite TV	$	$	$
Electric	$	$	$
Garbage	$	$	$
Gardener/landscaping	$	$	$
Gas	$	$	$
Heating oil/propane	$	$	$
Homeowners association	$	$	$
Home security (alarm company)	$	$	$
Housecleaning	$	$	$
HVAC	$	$	$

Continued on next page . . .

	Actual Amount (annual)	Budgeted Amount	Over or Under Amount
Internet access	$	$	$
Pest control	$	$	$
Phone (cellular)	$	$	$
Phone (landline)	$	$	$
Pool maintenance	$	$	$
Septic	$	$	$
Transit	$	$	$
Water/Sewer	$	$	$
Other utility/household expenses	$	$	$
Subtotal: Utility and Household Expenses	$	$	$

CARE AND SUPPORT—CHILD CARE, DAY CARE, TUITION, AND ADULT CARE

Child care	$	$	$
Day care	$	$	$
Tuition	$	$	$
Adult care	$	$	$
Other care and support expenses	$	$	$
Subtotal: Care and Support—Child Care, Day Care, Tuition, and Adult Care	$	$	$

SUBSCRIPTIONS AND DIGITAL SERVICES

Newspapers (physical and digital)	$	$	$
Magazines and periodicals (physical and digital)	$	$	$
Cloud storage	$	$	$
General web services	$	$	$
Music streaming	$	$	$
Video streaming	$	$	$
Gaming	$	$	$

	Actual Amount (annual)	Budgeted Amount	Over or Under Amount
Food and delivery services	$	$	$
Software subscriptions	$	$	$
Membership sites	$	$	$
Other subscriptions and digital services	$	$	$
Subtotal: Subscriptions and Digital Services	$	$	$

MEMBERSHIPS, SEASON TICKETS, CLUBS, AND ORGANIZATIONS

Auto club (AAA)	$	$	$
Gym	$	$	$
Service club	$	$	$
Season tickets	$	$	$
Other	$	$	$
Subtotal: Memberships, Season Tickets, Clubs, and Organizations	$	$	$

TAXES

Income taxes (federal, state, local, Social Security)	$	$	$
Property taxes	$	$	$
Other taxes	$	$	$
Subtotal: Taxes	$	$	$

INSURANCE

Group insurance premiums	$	$	$
Auto insurance	$	$	$
Disability insurance	$	$	$
Health insurance	$	$	$
Health care costs	$	$	$
Homeowners/renters insurance	$	$	$

Continued on next page . . .

	Actual Amount (annual)	Budgeted Amount	Over or Under Amount
Life insurance	$_____	$_____	$_____
Long-term care insurance	$_____	$_____	$_____
Annuity premiums	$_____	$_____	$_____
Other insurance premiums	$_____	$_____	$_____
Subtotal: Insurance	$_____	$_____	$_____
Total expenses	$_____	$_____	$_____
Total cash flow (total net income minus total expenses)	$_____	$_____	$_____

NEXT STEPS

Keep your cash flow statement current. You should update it at least once a year, preferably right after the first of the year while you are gathering your tax return information. This helps you track your cash flow by giving you a consistent reference point year after year. You should store a copy with your secure documents. You can add a copy to the financial readiness section of your GET READY! binder.

Tip

Create an emergency fund. Having cash reserves will help protect you from unexpected events, such as a loss of income or vital car repair. This fund should be enough to cover your living expenses for up to six months. There is no "magic" number. Just put aside what you feel will protect you if you were to lose your income for an extended period. This also provides funds so that your spouse or heirs can pay bills while your financial matters are settled, should you pass away.

Knowing Your Net Worth

Knowing your net worth will help you determine whether you are financially solvent and on track for a healthy financial life and retirement. It will also let you know if you need to make

FAIR MARKET VALUE/ CURRENT VALUE

In the net worth statement worksheet, you will estimate the fair market value of your assets. This is the price a willing buyer will pay a willing seller in a non-distressed sale environment. You may have financial statements that give you the current value of an asset (for example, a bank account or mutual fund shares). If not, you may need to get the current value from another source, such as eBay, or conduct your own evaluation, consulting financial references, advisors, or experts.

adjustments to your cash flow so that you can get on track. Your net worth is the total value of everything that you own (assets) less what you owe (liabilities). Your mission is to have more assets than liabilities and to grow your net worth so that you can retire and live comfortably, whatever that means to you.

The following worksheet allows you to gauge your net worth. If you followed the "Next steps" action items as you completed earlier chapters in this book, the worksheet will be easy to complete. You can also find this information on recent statements for each line item. All you'll need to do are some calculations. The more thoroughly you complete this worksheet, the more helpful it will be. You can also download this worksheet as an Excel file from www.tonysteuer.com/resources.

Net Worth Statement as of: _____

Assets (what you own)	Fair Market Value (estimated)
CASH AND LIQUID ASSETS	
Cash (at home—safe, wallet, etc.)	$
Checking account(s)	$
Savings account(s)	$
Certificate of deposit (CDs)	$
Money market account(s)	$
Annuity (surrender value)	$
Life insurance (surrender value)	$
Other liquid assets	$
Subtotal: Cash and Liquid Assets	**$**
INVESTED ASSETS	
Brokerage accounts	$
Stock	$
Treasury securities	$
Bonds	$
Mutual funds	$
Exchange-traded funds (ETFs)	$
Collectibles	$

Continued on next page . . .

Stock options	$
Business interests/ownerships	$
Royalties value (copyrights, trademarks, patents, other)	$
Debt and obligations owed to you	$
College savings accounts	$
ABLE accounts	$
Other assets	$
Subtotal: Invested Assets	$

RETIREMENT ASSETS

Individual retirement accounts (IRA & Roth IRA)	$
Self-employed and small business plans (KEOGH, SEP-IRA, SARSP IRA, Simple IRA, "solo" 401(k), and a defined-benefit plan)	$
401(k), 403(b) and 457 plan(s)	$
Pension lump sum benefit (vested amount)	$
Other employer and group retirement plan(s)	$
Other retirement accounts	$
Subtotal: Retirement Assets	$

PROPERTY

Home (primary residence)	$
Vacation home (secondary residence)	$
Investment property	$
Farmland	$
Undeveloped land	$
Commercial property	$
Car(s)	$
Planes, boats, and recreational vehicles	$
Computers	$
Entertainment (TVs and stereos)	$
Appliances	$

Other	$
Subtotal: Property	$
Total assets	$

LIABILITIES

CURRENT LIABILITIES

Auto loan(s)	$
Credit card(s)	$
Life insurance policy loan	$
Student loan	$
Other short-term loan	$
Subtotal: Current Liabilities	$

LONG-TERM LIABILITIES

Mortgage (primary residence)	$
Second mortgage	$
Home equity loan (HELOC)	$
Vacation home and time-share loan balance(s)	$
Reverse mortgage balance	$
Investment property loan balance(s)	$
Business property loan balance(s) (commercial)	$
Personal debts and loan balance(s)	$
Debt consolidation loan balance(s)	$
Other loan balance(s)	$
Subtotal: Long-Term Liabilities	$
Total liabilities	$
Net worth (total assets minus total liabilities)	$

Continued on next page . . . ➡

Tip

Make sure that you have the right type of insurance to protect each of your assets.

Retirement Planning Tracker

Retirement is not a magical event that happens on its own, nor is it something that is beyond your reach. It does, however, require some thought and savings. It's important to recognize that for most people, Social Security benefits alone will not be enough to fund their retirement. A sound retirement plan consists of more than just Social Security. You also need a full financial plan that you either work out with a qualified professional or put together yourself. If you do it yourself, it doesn't hurt to have a qualified financial planner review your plan at least once.

The earlier you start saving, the more money you will have. And at some point, age and health will play a part in when you retire from the work force or have to trim your hours worked. The average American will spend 20 plus years in retirement.

There are two parts to retirement planning: The first is determining a rough timeline for when you'd like to retire, and the second part is making sure you are on track to have enough money saved for retirement.

Your Retirement Timeline

For most of us, there is no set age for when we have to retire. We can choose to retire "early," which is usually considered before age 65, or to keep working. Age 65 is no longer a standard or mandatory retirement age. Some people retire well before 65, while many others continue to work either because they need the money or they like what they're doing.

Following are some dates to keep in mind when considering your retirement planning. Please add your own parameters, such as a mandatory retirement age, your preferred retirement age, and when you are vested in your pension.

Age 50

You can begin making catch-up contributions, an extra amount that those over age 50 can add to their 401(k) and other retirement accounts.

Age 59 ½

There are no more tax penalties on early withdrawals from employer-provided retirement savings plans such as 401(k)s and IRAs. Keep in mind that the longer you leave the money in, the more it will grow. Withdrawals are taxed as ordinary income.

Age 62

This is the earliest age to collect Social Security benefits. If you claim benefits earlier than your full retirement age, you will receive a lower monthly benefit.

Age 65

This is the age when you sign up for Medicare Parts A, B, and D, Medicare Supplements, or Medicare Advantage. This must be done within six months of turning 65. See details about Medicare on page 149.

Age 66 or Age 67

At this age you will receive full Social Security benefits, depending on your birth year. You can earn Social Security delayed retirement credits, which will increase your monthly benefit for each month that claiming is delayed between your full retirement age and age 70.

Age 70

Social Security benefits must be taken if claiming has been delayed.

Age 70 ½

You must start taking required minimum distributions (RMDs) from most retirement accounts at this age. If you do not, you may be charged significant penalties in the future.

Other:

In the space provided, list any other retirement dates that are important to you.

_____

_____

_____

HOW MUCH WILL YOU NEED
TO HAVE SAVED FOR RETIREMENT?

This is, of course, the most important question and the one that is subject to endless debate. There is no firm, one-size-fits-all answer, because there are so many unknowns, including longevity, rates of return, and unforeseen expenses. Therefore, when you are planning for your retirement, it is best to be conservative, as it is better to have too much money in retirement than too little.

The following worksheet will help give you a general idea of where you are currently with your retirement planning and help you plan out any changes. Having your retirement planning in focus is a key factor in organizing your financial life and your estimated retirement financials.

Part A: Where are you now?

Step 1: Enter your desired retirement age: _____

Step 2: Decide how much you will need for retirement. Calculate your estimated monthly expenses in retirement. You can use your current annual expenses (from page 198) or make adjustments, as your needs may change.

Enter your estimated monthly expenses: $_____

Note

While everyone's situation during retirement is different, a safe approach is to plan on needing the same amount of income you have today. Add up all of your essential annual expenses, including housing, health care, food, utilities, and taxes. Then estimate discretionary expenses such as travel, gifts, dining out, hobbies, and recreation. Certain costs, such as mortgages and work-related expenses, may decrease in retirement; others, such as health care costs and travel, may increase. If you would like to adjust for inflation, you can easily do so by using a future-value calculator.

Step 3: Calculate your annual retirement income.

Add up your estimated income from predictable streams of income, such as Social Security, annuity payments, pensions, and any rental income you may be receiving. To estimate your income from a retirement account, there are two choices: 1) Your plan sponsor (e.g. Vanguard or Fidelity) will usually provide an estimated income stream that you will receive from a 401(k) or 403(b), and you can use that number. You'll typically receive two figures, one if you were to not fund the plan further and the other if you were to continue to fund the plan up to a specific age (usually age 54). You should use whichever figure best meets your needs. For any estimates that are provided on a monthly basis, multiply by 12 to use an annual estimate. 2) The other choice is to make a conservative estimate that your income will be 3% of the total current balance. With this option, you'll multiply the balance of the account by 3% and use that figure.

Estimate your annual retirement income by filling in the amounts below:

Social security (see the note at the bottom of page 76 for details on ordering a social security statement): $_____

Estimated monthly payment: $_____ x 12 =
estimated annual payment: $_____.

Pension plan(s): current account balance of $_____.
Estimated annual income: $_____.

Veteran's benefits: current account balance of $_____.
Estimated annual income: $_____.

Employer retirement plan (e.g. 401(k), 457, 403(b)): current account balance(s) of
$_____.
Estimated annual income: $_____.

Individual retirement plan (e.g. IRA, Roth IRA, KEOGH, SEP-IRA, SARSEP IRA): current
account balance of $_____.
Estimated annual income: $_____.

Income from investments (stocks, bonds, mutual funds, ETFs): current account balance of
$_____.
Estimated annual income: $_____.

Earnings (salary, consulting fees, royalties): current account balance of $_____.
Estimated annual income: $_____.

Take your income and reduce by taxes (if taxes are not included in expenses):

Total pre-tax annual income (all categories above) $_____

Less: Federal income taxes $_____

Less: State income taxes $_____

Step 4: Estimate your retirement surplus or shortfall (subtract expenses from income,
step 3 minus step 2): $_____

If you have a shortfall, you'll need to either save more or lower your expenses. Progress to part B.

Part B: Addressing the shortfall

The following steps will allow you to calculate how much you will need to save each year to close your
retirement gap.

Step 5: To estimate the total amount of additional money you need to save, beyond your
current contributions, multiply your shortfall (from step 4) by the appropriate
factor* below: $_____

*Anticipated retirement age:

55: multiply by 21.0

Continued on next page . . . ➡

60: multiply by 18.9

65: multiply by 16.4

70: multiply by 13.6

Step 6: Enter the current total value of your savings (investment accounts and retirement accounts) from your net worth statement: $_____

Step 7: Estimate the projected value of your retirement accounts and other assets at retirement age: $_____

Multiply figure from step 6 by the appropriate factor*, as follows: $_____

*Years until retirement:

10 years: multiply by 1.3

15 years: multiply by 1.6

20 years: multiply by 1.8

25 years: multiply by 2.1

30 years: multiply by 2.4

35 years: multiply by 2.8

40 years: multiply by 3.3

Step 8: Find your estimated amount of savings needed at retirement. To do this, enter the estimated additional amount you need to save (from step 5), and subtract your current estimated value of assets at retirement (from step 7): $_____

Step 9: Calculate the additional estimated gross amount that you'll need to save each year. Multiply the result from step 8 by the appropriate factor* below: $_____

*Retiring in:

10 years: multiply by 0.085

15 years: multiply by 0.052

20 years: multiply by 0.036

25 years: multiply by 0.027

30 years: multiply by 0.020

35 years: multiply by 0.016

40 years: multiply by 0.013

Step 10: Add the total of your current annual contributions to your retirement plans (IRAs, 401(k)s, and others): $_____

Step 11: Calculate the net additional amount that you'll need to save each year by subtracting the total of your current annual contributions (Step 10) from the gross annual amount of savings needed each year (Step 9): $_____

Tip

There are many retirement savings calculators online that you can access. Use these calculators at your discretion, however, as they will each provide weighted results. If you are investing with a firm, such as Vanguard, Schwab, or Fidelity, you can find calculators on their sites, and you may want to go with these instead. Remember that you must enter accurate information to get useful results.

Note

Health care costs will be a big factor in retirement. For individuals retiring in 2018, a male will need $133,000 to cover health care costs in retirement. Females will need $147,000, primarily due to the fact that women are expected to live longer than men.

FINANCIAL RATIOS

Financial ratios are general guidelines to see if your financial life is on a healthy, organized track. Everyone's situation is different, so if your ratios aren't in line with the recommended ratios, make adjustments that will meet your needs and goals. Use these ratios as guidelines to mark your progress. The worksheets that you've completed will help you calculate your financial ratios and help you assess where you currently are with your financial life.

Emergency fund: cash on hand

The following figures can be found on your cash flow statement. Enter them below to determine your current emergency fund:

Fixed monthly expenses (housing, insurance, utilities, car payments): $_____

Liquid cash (checking account, savings account, or other): $_____

Divide fixed monthly expenses by your available liquid cash: _____

Goal: This fund should include any months that you would be able to cover emergency expenses such as loss of income.

Continued on next page . . .

Liquidity ratio

The following figures can be found on your net worth statement. Enter them below to determine your current liquidity ratio:

Total net worth: $_____

Liquid assets (cash & near cash assets and other marketable securities & assets that can be liquidated within three to four working days): $_____

Divide total net worth by your liquid assets: $_____

Goal: The liquidity ratio should be at least 15 percent. This works together with your emergency fund.

Debt-to-income ratio

The following figures can be found on your cash flow statement. Enter them below to determine your current debt-to-income ratio:

Gross income: $_____

Step 1: Total housing costs (principal, interest, taxes, and insurance): $_____

Step 2: Divide by gross income: _____

Desired total range is 28 percent.

Step 3: Add total housing costs plus other debt: $_____

Step 4: Divide by gross income: $_____

Goal: Your desired total range is 36 percent. Lenders use these ratios to determine the largest amount of debt that is acceptable.

Savings ratio

The following figures can be found on your cash flow statement. Enter them below to determine your current savings ratio, which should be in line with the results from the retirement tracker:

Amount you save each month (savings, investments, and retirement plans): $_____

Gross income (all forms of income): $_____

Amount you save each month divided by your gross income: $_____

Goal: This ratio should be between 12–20 percent. This ratio has a wide range as it depends on your current age, your desired retirement age, and how much you've already saved.

Net worth ratio

The following figures can be found on your cash flow statement. Enter them below to determine your current net worth ratio:

Annual gross income (from all sources): $_____

Age: _____

Multiply your annual gross income by your age: $_____

Divide by 10.

Goal: The sum should equal your net worth. Your earning power will be impacted by the choices you make; for example, if you went for an advanced educational degree, you will be starting work later but will expect to have higher future earnings. This ratio is from the book *The Millionaire Next Door.*

 END-OF-PLANNER CHECK-IN

Did this planner help you GET READY!? In the following table, assess your level of financial preparedness by checking the appropriate status box for all the topics in this planner (as broken down by chapter).

Chapter 2: Creating Your Financial First Aid Kit

	In Progress	Completed	Not Applicable
Emergency contact list			
Personal papers & legal documents master list			
Critical emergency action list			
Contents of wallet			
Storing documents and valuables			
Personal information			
Children			
Grandchildren			
Health information (medical)			
Pet information			
Military service			
Memberships: clubs and organizations			
Charitable organizations			
Digital life (devices and services)			
Reward and loyalty programs			

Chapter 3: Listing Your Assets (Non-retirement)

	In Progress	Completed	Not Applicable
Checking and savings accounts			
Certificate(s) of deposit (CD)			
Stocks			
Treasury securities (bills & bonds)			
Corporate bonds, government agency bonds, and municipal bonds			
Mutual funds			
Exchange-traded funds			
Collectibles			
Stock options			
Business interests/ownerships			
Royalties			
Debts and obligations			
College savings accounts			
ABLE accounts			

Chapter 4: Organizing Your Retirement Plan

	In Progress	Completed	Not Applicable
Individual retirement accounts (IRAs)			
Self-employed and small business retirement accounts			
401(k), 403(b), and 457 plans			
Pension plans			
Other employer retirement plans			
Social Security			

Chapter 5: Listing Your Home and Real Estate/Real Property

	In Progress	Completed	Not Applicable
Home (primary residence)			
Vacation home/secondary residence			
Time-share/vacation club			
Investment property			
Farmland			
Undeveloped land			
Commercial property			
Cars			
Planes, boats, and recreational vehicles			
Personal property inventory			

Chapter 6: Compiling Your Income (Earnings)

	In Progress	Completed	Not Applicable
Employer compensation			
Paid time off			
Group (employee) benefits			
Dependents coverage			
Other earned income			
Online income/sales			
Royalties			
Investment income			
Retirement income			

Chapter 7: Organizing Your Debts, Personal Loans, Living Expenses, and Taxes

	In Progress	Completed	Not Applicable
Car loans and leases			
Home loan (mortgage)			
Private mortgage insurance			
Vacation home and time-share loans			
Reverse mortgage			
Student loans			
Investment and business property loans			
Personal loans and debts (miscellaneous)			
Credit cards			
Debt consolidation loans			
Living expenses			
Education, care, and support (child care, day care, tuition, and adult care)			
Subscriptions and services			
Memberships, season tickets, clubs, and organizations			
Taxes			

Chapter 8: Assembling Your Insurance Portfolio

	In Progress	Completed	Not Applicable
Auto insurance			
Disability insurance			
Health insurance			
Homeowners and renters insurance			
Life insurance			

	In Progress	Completed	Not Applicable
Long-term care insurance			
Annuities			
Other insurance coverage			

Chapter 9: Estate Planning

	In Progress	Completed	Not Applicable
Power(s) of attorney			
Advanced/health care directives			
Letter of intent			
Organ or body donations			
Burial and cremation			
Funeral and memorial services			
Obituary			
Ethical will			
Will (and last testament)			
Trusts			
Digital estate planning			
Pet estate planning			

Chapter 10: Evaluating Your Financial Readiness

	In Progress	Completed	Not Applicable
Cash flow statement and budget			
Net worth statement			
Retirement planning tracker			
Financial ratios			

 **PRINT FORMS**

To print these forms, visit my website at www.tonysteuer.com/resources.

NOTES

_____

_____

_____

_____

_____

_____

_____

_____

_____

_____

_____

_____

_____

_____

_____

_____

_____

_____

_____

_____

_____

_____

CHAPTER 11

Staying Ready

Plan your work for today and every day, then work your plan.
—MARGARET THATCHER

In your regular life, between emergencies and first aid situations, you'll need to periodically review your first aid kit and refresh your supplies. Just as your physical first aid kit needs to be current, your financial emergency kit also needs to be kept "fresh." Life is full of change, and some things, such as a marriage or birth of a child, can cause a ripple effect throughout your financial life. There is also the usual ongoing monitoring to make sure that everything is on track and continues to work as you expect it to. You don't want any surprises when it's too late to make a change. Knowing your financial weak points will enable you to fix them. If you don't know what they are, they will always be vulnerable and at risk of being exploited.

Gathering and assessing the information in this chapter will help you ensure accuracy about your financial records and allow you to "fix" any issues that surface during your assessment. For example, you should review your credit reports, which are used for multiple purposes and will affect the interest rates you receive on loans, insurance premiums, and more.

 GET READY!

In this chapter, we'll review ways you can stay financially ready. While organizing this part of the planner, you will learn about—

1. **Financial review calendar.** You will be creating a calendar so that you can periodically review the various parts of your financial life.

2. **Credit report monitoring.** You'll also be guided through ordering credit reports and other financial reports to make sure that your public financial information is accurate and up to date. And you'll learn how to spot identity theft, how your credit score is calculated, and the names of specialty consumer reporting agencies.

Financial Calendar

Having continuity and a plan to deal with repeating occurrences in your financial life will help you stay ready and will actually save you time and effort. Setting up your financial calendar will help to ensure that you don't miss any important dates and that you are regularly monitoring what needs to be reviewed, allowing you to maximize your finances and minimize your expenses. This will help you tell your best financial story.

Use the following financial calendar to remind you about items that occur annually (some are already added to get you started). Add your own items where you feel they work best. For one-time events such as a loan payoff date, enter it in the financial one-time events section. You may also want to add these items to any to-do planners or calendars that you currently use. When you complete these items, be sure to update this calendar and refresh your GET READY! binder.

January

- Organize your financial documents and receipts and update this PLANNER. This will help you prepare for filing your taxes.
- Review your net worth and budget/cash flow (personal balance sheet). This lets you see how you did last year and if you want to make any changes for the new year.
- Pay estimated Q4 (fourth-quarter) taxes from prior year (if applicable).

  - _____
  - _____
  - _____
  - _____

February

- Organize tax documents and receipts that will be needed for filing taxes.

  - _____
  - _____
  - _____
  - _____

March

- This is your flexible spending account claim deadline (for the prior calendar year), as FSAs are "use or lose." This can vary by plan, so check your plan for specifics. Dependent care spending accounts allow you to carry over a limited amount (changes). Health savings accounts allow you to carry over your full balance.
- Review your retirement plan contributions and balances.

- Review your investments and allocations. Make sure they are still in line with your retirement goals.
- IRAs and 401(k)s have a required minimum distribution (RMD) of April 1 if you turned age 70 ½ during the prior calendar year. If you are nearing this age, you will want to stay on top of this to avoid being assessed a penalty. Please note that there may be exceptions.

   ◦ _____
   ◦ _____
   ◦ _____
   ◦ _____

April

- File federal and state income tax returns. Tax returns are due on April 15 (if April 15 is on a weekend, the IRS and individual states usually extend the due date to the following Monday, but check the IRS and your state's tax websites to confirm). Request extension(s) if necessary. States have different rules, so check with your state tax authority. Fines and penalties can be assessed for missing deadlines.
- Pay estimated Q1 taxes (if applicable).
- Your IRA contribution deadline for prior calendar year is this month.

   ◦ _____
   ◦ _____
   ◦ _____
   ◦ _____

May

- Order annual credit reports.

   ◦ _____
   ◦ _____
   ◦ _____
   ◦ _____

June

- Pay estimated Q2 taxes (if applicable).

   ◦ _____
   ◦ _____
   ◦ _____
   ◦ _____

July

- Request Social Security benefit statements to ensure earnings are reported correctly so that your benefits will be accurate.
- Have a family financial meeting to discuss your GET READY! planner and financial life.

  - _____
  - _____
  - _____
  - _____

August

- Review estate plan and estate planning documents to make sure they are current. This includes wills, trusts, and advance directives.

  - _____
  - _____
  - _____
  - _____

September

- Pay estimated Q3 taxes (if applicable). Make sure you are on track with what you may owe in taxes.
- Review insurance policies and, if applicable, prepare for open enrollment (if insurance policies have an expiration date, then add them to the appropriate month). Make sure coverage still meets your needs and adjust accordingly.
- Review retirement plan contributions and projections to see if you are on target and if you need to adjust contributions and to prepare for open enrollment.
- Consider if beneficiary updates are needed for retirement accounts and insurance policies.

  - _____
  - _____
  - _____
  - _____

October

- If you filed for a tax extension, your deadline to file is October 15 (if October 15 falls on a weekend, this will usually be extended to the following Monday—check the IRS and state websites).

_____

_____

_____

_____

November

- Open enrollment for group employee benefits (if applicable) usually starts in October and ends in December. This includes insurance, retirement, spending accounts, and other benefits.

_____

_____

_____

_____

December

- Individual health care enrollment deadline for Federal Health Insurance Exchange is December 15—visit healthcare.gov. States with their own exchanges may have longer open enrollment periods, so check your state website as well. If you experience a major life event (or meet other specific criteria), you may also be able to apply for health insurance during special enrollment periods.

- Charitable donations. Make any year-end donations to support your favorite nonprofits to make a positive difference and to be able to claim your tax deduction.

- Complete any gifts to people or trusts to take advantage of the annual gift tax exclusion. The annual gift tax exclusion limits increase each year.

- Review your IRA and 401(k) contributions and distributions. If you had to take a first RMD by April 1, you must take your second RMD by December 31.

_____

_____

_____

_____

NEXT STEPS

After you review each item in your financial calendar (page 216), be sure to update the appropriate section in this planner and in your GET READY! binder. (You can also keep a copy in the staying ready section of your GET READY! binder.) You can also download the financial calendar from www.tonysteuer.com/resources.

Financial One-Time Events

Some events will only occur once—such as the date a CD matures or the date you pay off a loan. You can enter these events in the table below. You may also wish to enter these dates on any to-do planners or calendars that you currently use.

Name of Event	Date

Note

There will be events through your life when you will need to update the GET READY! binder and financial calendar. These include any change to items already listed in this planner and may include—

- Change in marital status
- Addition to the family (birth or adoption of a child)
- Death of a family member
- Disability
- Opening or closing of a bank account or other financial account
- Purchasing a home or renting an apartment (moving)
- Changing insurance companies
- Retirement planning
- Estate planning
- Change in tax laws

Tip

Something that I like to do every year or two is to look for unclaimed property. Each state has enacted an unclaimed property statute that protects your funds from reverting back to the company if you have lost contact with them. These laws instruct companies to turn forgotten funds over to a state official who will then make a diligent effort to find you or your heirs. Most states hold lost funds until you are found, returning them to you at no cost or for a nominal handling fee after you've filed a claim form and they've successfully verified your identity. Since it is impossible to store and maintain all of the contents that are turned over from safe-deposit boxes, most states hold periodic auctions and collect the funds obtained from the sale of the items for the owner.

Some states also sell stocks and bonds and return the proceeds to the owner in the same manner. The National Association of Unclaimed Property Administrators (NAUPA) has a website with more information and links to your state's unclaimed property website; visit www.unclaimed.org. NAUPA and participating states and provinces have officially endorsed MissingMoney.com. On their site, you can search all participating states to find your family's missing, lost, and unclaimed property, money, and assets. Searches and claims are always free. Information goes securely and directly to the state/provincial unclaimed property office.

Be aware: There are many services and sites that will attempt to charge you money to search for your property when you can use the MissingMoney.com and state websites for free.

There are specialized websites you can use, such as the National Association of Insurance Commissioner's Life Insurance Policy locator service at https://eapps.naic.org/life-policy-locator, to search for life insurance and annuity contracts for deceased family members and close relatives. Visit www.tonysteuer.com/resources for more free online services.

Protecting Your Information: Credit Report Monitoring

Credit reports are compiled by credit reporting agencies, which are companies that collect information about where you live and work, how you pay your bills, and whether or not you have been sued, been arrested, or filed for bankruptcy. These companies sell your credit report to creditors, employers, insurers, and others. These companies will use these reports to make decisions about extending credit, jobs, and insurance policies to you.

Tip

You are entitled to order a free copy of your credit report from each of the major credit reporting agencies (Equifax, Experian, and TransUnion) every 12 months at www.annualcreditreport.com (or by calling (877) 322-8228). This website is the only one that is government authorized to provide you with free copies of your credit report. **Beware:** There are many sites with similar URLs that will either attempt to charge you or steal your personal information.

You can also contact the credit agencies directly if you need to dispute information in your report, need to place a fraud alert or security freeze on your credit file, or have other questions:

- Equifax (www.equifax.com or (866) 349-5191)
- Experian (www.experian.com or (888) 397-3742)
- TransUnion (www.transunion.com or (800) 916-8800)

Navigating Your Credit Report

Next, we are going to navigate your credit report. Use the following worksheet to guide you through the process. In the columns following, add "Yes" if that section is correct or "No" if there is an error. See the Tip following the table for guidance on dealing with errors found in your credit reports.

Credit Agency	Equifax	Experian	Transunion
Date of report			
Name (check spelling)			
Social Security number			
Current address and phone number			
Marital status			
Other personal history information			
Employment history			
Public record information			
Credit card account status (open or closed)			
Current balances			
Missing accounts for which you are an authorized user or joint owner listed			
If any bankruptcies, check that zero balances are recorded for debts discharged in bankruptcy and for debts paid in full			
Names of accounts that you closed that are not listed as "closed by the consumer"			
If negative information, make sure missed payments and/or late payments are listed correctly			
Accounts listed more than once (also check the collections section)			
Old/negative information still being reported beyond limit (usually 7 years)			
Any reason to suspect identity theft?			
Make sure that any loans for which you are listed as a co-signer are accurate			
Document location*			
Website, user name, password, secret question			
Notes:			

Tip

You should check all of these reports annually to ensure they are accurate and to spot any unauthorized activity. You'll also want to make sure that all accounts and other information listed for you on these reports is accurate and complete. Be sure to also review account status reporting, as status and dates can be incorrect, or debts can be listed twice.

You are probably the only person who can verify the accuracy of these reports. If you find something wrong with your credit report, you can file your dispute online at each credit reporting agency's website.

Explain what you think is wrong and why, along with any documentation to support your case. There may be certain circumstances in which creditors and furnishing institutions are not required to investigate, but it is always worth pursuing.

Identity Theft

Now that you've looked over your recent credit reports, I want to cover the important topic of identity theft so that you are armed with information and know what to do should it ever happen to you or a loved one. Identity theft refers to any fraudulent activity that could entail using your personal information without your permission, such as your name, Social Security number, or credit card number. Your Social Security number is the most important piece of information a bank needs when extending credit or opening an account. Social Security numbers can be used to obtain medical care, file a fraudulent tax return, commit crimes, or steal your Social Security benefits. Your credit card number can be used to make unauthorized purchases (though you may be protected). Review your credit card and banking statements each month. Contact your bank or credit card company if you notice suspicious activity on any of your accounts. You may ask them to put a security block on your account or preemptively request a new credit or debit card if you find any suspicious activity.

Tip

If you suspect that an error on your credit report is a result of identity theft, visit the Federal Trade Commission's IdentityTheft.gov website for information about identity theft and steps to take if you have been victimized. This will include filing a fraud alert and possibly filing a security freeze with the three main credit reporting agencies (Equifax, Experian, and TransUnion).

A "security freeze" on your credit report prevents new creditors from accessing your credit file and others from opening accounts in your name until you lift the freeze. Because most businesses will not open credit accounts without checking your credit report, a freeze can stop identity thieves from opening new accounts in your name.

Monitoring and organizing your financial life is an important step toward protecting your identity. You can also protect yourself by not carrying your Social Security card, shredding pre-approved credit card offers and bills before disposing of them, and being careful of where you use credit cards online (make sure you have a secure connection to a legitimate website).

Credit Scores

Every credit report shows your current credit score. Your credit score is important, as it predicts how likely you are to pay back a loan on time. Companies use a mathematical formula, called a scoring model, to create your credit score from the information in your credit report, which is why it is important to check your credit reports each year to ensure all the information is current and correct. It is also important to know that you do not have just "one" credit score and there are many credit scores available to you as well as to lenders. For example, each credit reporting agency has its own unique credit score. The Fair Isaac Corporation, which has the most well-known and probably oldest credit score (FICO), now offers lenders 28 different scores, for example.

Any credit score depends on the data used to calculate it, and your score may differ depending on the scoring model, the source of your credit history, the type of loan product, and even the day it was calculated. Lenders look at many things when making a credit decision, such as your income, how long you have worked at your present job, and the kind of credit you are requesting. Here's a breakdown on how your FICO score is created:

- **Payment history (35%).** The first thing any lender wants to know is whether you've paid past credit accounts on time. This is one of the most important factors in a FICO score.

- **Amounts owed (30%).** Having credit accounts and owing money on them does not necessarily mean you are a high-risk borrower with a low FICO score.

- **Length of credit history (15%).** In general, a longer credit history will increase your FICO scores. However, even people who haven't been using credit long may have high FICO scores, depending on how the rest of the credit report looks. Your FICO scores take into account how long your credit accounts have been established, including the age of your oldest account; the age of your newest account and an average age of all your accounts; how long specific credit accounts have been established; and how long it has been since you used certain accounts.

- **Credit mix in use (10%).** FICO scores will consider your mix of credit cards, retail accounts, installment loans, finance company accounts, and mortgage loans.

- **New credit (10%).** Research shows that opening several credit accounts in a short period of time represents a greater risk—especially for people who don't have a long credit history.

Tip

An easy way to get your free FICO score is via the Discover credit scorecard (https://www.credit-scorecard.com). You do not need to be a customer of Discover. Anyone can register and get their official FICO score for free here. The data is from the Experian credit bureau. Also, an increasing number of credit card companies, identity protection services, and the like now include a complimentary credit score. Keep in mind that most of these are not the true FICO score that lenders subscribe to and use as part of their decision-making process.

Specialty Consumer Reporting Companies

As you may know, there are many entities tracking and compiling information on you. While that may sound paranoid, it is the reality we all live in. Along with Facebook and Google, there are many specialty consumer-reporting companies that collect and share information about your employment history, transaction history with a business, or your repayment history for a specific product or service. The federal Fair Credit Reporting Act (FCRA) promotes the accuracy, fairness, and privacy of information in the files of consumer reporting agencies.

Here are four reports that you should consider requesting each year, in addition to your annual credit reports from the three major credit bureaus:

- **LexisNexis.** They compile information to create consumer reports. This includes items such as real estate transactions and ownership data; lien, judgment, and bankruptcy records; professional license information; and historical addresses on file. Request your report (https://personalreports.lexisnexis.com).

- **C.L.U.E. Report.** Also from LexisNexis, this includes information on insurance claims histories for auto insurance and homeowners insurance. Request your report (https://personalreports.lexisnexis.com/fact_act_disclosure.jsp).

- **Medical Information Bureau (MIB).** You will have an MIB file if you have applied for individual life insurance, disability insurance, or health insurance in the last seven years. MIB records contain coded information identifying any medical conditions or medical tests reported by other MIB members regarding that applicant. It does not have actual "reports" or "medical records" on file. There are also a few codes that identify dangerous hobbies or a driving record showing bad driving history. Request your report (https://www.mib.com/request_your_record.html).

- **The Work Number.** Also from Equifax, this report compiles employment and income information. It is used by lenders, property managers, pre-employment screeners, social service agencies, and others who need to verify someone's employment status and sometimes his or her income as well. Request your report (www.theworknumber.com).

> **NEXT STEPS**
>
> If you plan to order these reports annually, you should also add the specific report names to your financial calendar at the beginning of this chapter.

Tip

To learn more, visit www.tonysteuer.com/consumer-reporting-companies for a list of most of the common and not-so-common companies that compile information about you.

END-OF-CHAPTER CHECK-IN

Did this chapter help you GET READY!? In the following table, assess your level of financial preparedness by checking the appropriate status box for all the topics in this chapter.

	In Progress	Completed	Not Applicable
Financial review calendar			
Credit report monitoring			

PRINT FORMS

To print these forms, visit my website at www.tonysteuer.com/resources.

NOTES

Final Words

I am prepared for the worst but hope for the best.
—Benjamin Disraeli

Congratulations on completing the setup of your GET READY! planner and, if you've so chosen, your GET READY! binder. Staying ready is an ongoing task. However, taking the first step is often the hardest part.

You'll want to revisit your binder often to update it as your life changes. For example, if you've paid off a loan or taken on additional debt, you will need to update the planner to reflect these changes. I recommend that you visit your financial calendar monthly to see what changes or updates you can make. I also recommend that you relay any updates to family members who will be overseeing your estate in the event of your passing so that everyone can stay in the know.

I invite you to visit my website www.tonysteuer.com for additional tips and updates. In addition, you will find updated forms that you can download or print. Sign up for the GET READY! newsletter to receive tips and resources to help you maintain your financial first aid kit and keep up to date on the latest in financial preparedness.

And lastly, I welcome your feedback on the binder. Since I will be updating the forms each year, it will be helpful to know what has (and hasn't) worked for you.

Wishing you all good things and continued financial success,
Tony Steuer, CLU, LA, CPFFE; author and financial consumer advocate

Stepping In

Someone's sitting in the shade today because someone planted a tree a long time ago.
—WARREN BUFFETT

In an emergency situation, the rescuer can become someone also in need of rescuing. This means that another person will have to step in and potentially use your emergency first aid kit. If your emergency first aid is organized in a way that can be recognized by other rescuers, they will be able to step in immediately and help out. Every minute counts in an emergency situation, and the time saved by being organized and having everything clearly outlined will make a positive difference in the outcome.

In the event that you are the personal representative (executor or trustee) for the person who's completed this planner, the following action steps can help you wrap up their financial life. You can also print out this list at www.tonysteuer.com/resources.

 Note

This is not a complete list, and some items may not be applicable to your situation. Also, these steps do not need to be taken in this particular order.

Steps to Take	Status
Arrange for care of immediate family, including appropriate child care and having people at decedent's house.	
Call key family members and friends to notify them of your loved one's passing (find list on page 178).	
Contact funeral home and clergy/other to make an appointment to discuss funeral arrangements. See letter of instruction and obituary information on pages 176 and 181.	
Contact the deceased's and spouse's employer and company.	

Continued on next page . . .

Steps to Take	Status
Contact neighbors.	
If no surviving spouse or domestic partner, file a change of address form for mail to be sent to the personal representative.	
Arrange for cleaning of the home.	
Contact professional advisors to assess the family's needs (e.g., accountant, financial planner, attorney).	
Open an estate checking account.	
Establish access to emergency cash reserves to cover family needs and expenses over the next six weeks. See bank/investment accounts and passwords on pages 41 and 13.	
Review recurring monthly household and business expenses, including manual vs. auto-pay; see passwords; contact creditors, local utilities, and other services on page 130.	
Keep track of expenses incurred on behalf of the estate, as these will be used for income and estate tax purposes.	
Gather all statements and other important mail to assist with locating and organizing information.	
Locate important estate planning documents.	
Locate important account information, including bank and financial institutions, life insurance policies, beneficiary designation forms, prenuptial agreements, partnership and other business agreements, and location of passwords.	
Contact the Social Security Administration to notify them of the death and to inquire about benefits. If you are using a funeral home, they will make the report if you provide them with the decedent's Social Security number.	
Get an employer tax ID number for the estate. (IRS Form SS-4)	
Contact the Veterans Administration if you believe they are entitled to benefits and inclusion in funeral arrangements.	
If decedent is over age 65, contact the local Medicare office to notify them of the passing.	
Contact life, long-term care, accident, disability, and health insurance.	
Contact financial institutions where the safe-deposit boxes are located.	

Steps to Take	Status
Contact creditors to notify them of the passing of the decedent.	
Contact banks and other financial institutions to notify them of the passing of the decedent; review titles on all accounts and assets.	
Open probate if required (or file small estate affidavit if applicable).	
Arrange for the filing of the decedent's final tax return (Form 1041) and estate tax return.	
Report death to the three national credit reporting agencies by phone. Request the report is flagged as "Deceased. Do not issue credit." Follow up in writing by certified mail with these agencies.	
Safeguard decedent's valuables.	
Cancel decedent's subscriptions.	
Collect all decedent's credit cards so they cannot be used.	
Distribute payments to heirs and creditors carefully.	
Notes:	

Tip

Contact the county or state vital records office in the place where the death occurred to find out what is needed to order death certificates. Get at least 10 certified copies of the death certificate. You will need them for insurance claims, funeral, and other reasons (such as transferring accounts to a spouse's name, etc.). You will be surprised at how helpful it is to have multiple copies of this one document.

Note

Safeguard valuables. As executor, it's your job to keep estate assets safe until you turn them over to the people who inherit them. Lots of people will probably be coming and going, and things can "disappear." So, if the decedent's home contains cash, valuable jewelry, art, collections, or other similar items, make sure they are locked away. If relatives or friends pressure you to let them take a "keepsake" or something they say was promised to them, explain that legally you can't give anything away yet.

Maintain all real property such as cars and homes. Continue to make timely payments on any loans, insurance premiums, and local property tax bills to avoid penalties or default. If the insurance lapses and there is a personal injury claim, you may end up being personally liable for the loss. It's also your obligation to make sure that cars and homes receive basic regular maintenance until you are able to sell or redistribute them, based on the decedent's wishes in their will, if available.

Pay all bills from estate assets. Avoid commingling your own money with that of the estate, if at all possible.

Distribute payments to creditors. You have no obligation to pay off any debts of the deceased unless you are a responsible party on the account. Creditors must be paid in the right way, in order, and at the right time. Depending on state law, you may need to wait a specified period for bills to come in and post a public notice of death in a newspaper before you start distributing money. It's important to pay all debt out of the assets of the estate. If you waste estate assets, misuse them, or otherwise fail to follow established procedures, as personal representative (executor), you can be found liable for debts owed. So do your research and make no promises or agreements. You can find resources on acting as an executor or hiring a professional executor at https://www.nolo.com /legal-encyclopedia/executor-faq.html.

NOTES

A Note from the Author

Dear Reader,

Thank you for taking the time to learn about risk protection for your financial life. I hope you are feeling organized and ready for any financial situation with your GET READY! kit.

Financial preparedness is the most important part of emergency preparedness, as being financially organized allows you to recover more easily from physical setbacks that could be endured in a disaster, as well as keep you prepared for life's inevitable changes, such as the passing away of a loved one.

If you loved the book and have a minute to spare, I would really appreciate a short review on your favorite book site. You're the reason why I continue to write about financial preparedness and advocate for integrity in financial services.

If you think this book might help a family member or friend with their own financial preparedness, feel free to invite them to take a complimentary Financial Preparedness Assessment at www.tonysteuer. com. They'll receive a financial preparedness score and weekly email tips to show them how they might complete a planner of their own.

So what's next? Take the financial preparedness assessment, and stay up to date on the latest in financial preparedness by subscribing to the GET READY! Newsletter and joining our community.

Thank you!

Tony

INDEX

A

ABLE (Achieving a Better Life Experience) accounts, 62–63
ABLE National Resource Center, 62
ACA (Affordable Care Act), 148
accidental death and dismemberment insurance, 167
accumulation phase, annuities, 165
actual cash value policy, property insurance, 158
adult care
    cash flow statement, 196
    living expenses, 132–33
Advanced Directive, 174–75
advisory costs, investment, 40
Affordable Care Act (ACA), 148
AFR (applicable federal rate), 60
AM Best rating agency, 142
American Animal Hospital Association, 28
American Resort Development Association (ARDA), 116
annuities, 164–66
    accumulation phase, 165
    fixed, 164
    indexed, 164
    payout phase, 165
    variable, 164
    withdrawals from, 164
applicable federal rate (AFR), 60
ARDA (American Resort Development Association), 116
assets
    ABLE accounts, 62–63
    bank accounts, 40–42
    bonds, 46–50
        callable bonds, 46
        corporate bonds, 48–50
        coupon rate, 46
        discount rate, 46
        face value, 46
        government agency bonds, 48–50
        maturity, 46
        municipal bonds, 48–50
        price, 46
        quality rating, 46
        Series EE savings bonds, 48
        Series I savings bonds, 48
        short-term bonds, 46
        Treasury securities, 46–48
        yield, 46
    business interests/ownerships, 56–57
    certificates of deposit, 42–43
    check-in gauge, 63–64, 210
    collectibles, 53–54
    college savings accounts, 60–61
    debts and loans, 59–60
    document retention schedule, 13
    exchange-traded funds, 52–53
    mutual funds, 50–52
    net worth statement, 199–201
        cash, 199
        invested assets, 199–200
        liquid assets, 199
        property, 200–201
        retirement assets, 200
    overview, 39–40
    real estate/real property, 14–15, 79–93
        boats, 89–90
        cars, 88–89
        check-in gauge, 93, 211
        commercial property, 87
        farmland, 85–86
        inventory of major property, 91–93
        investment property, 84–85
        net worth statement, 200–201
        overview, 79–80
        ownership, 40, 172
        planes, 89–90
        primary residence, 80–81
        recreational vehicles, 89–90
        time-share, 83–84
        unclaimed property, 221
        undeveloped land, 86
        vacation home, 82
    royalties, 57–58
    stock options, 54–56
    stocks, 44–45
auto insurance, 142–45

B

bank accounts, 40, 42
beneficiaries

ABLE accounts, 62
    college savings accounts, 60
    contingent, 159, 173
    defined, 173
    employment retirement accounts, 71
    IRAs, 67
    letter of intent/instruction for, 176
    life insurance, 159
    small-employed and small business IRAs, 69
    trusts, 185–86
bequests, 183, 184
birth certificates, storing, 25
boats, 89–90
bonds, 46–50
    callable bonds, 46
    corporate bonds, 48–50
    coupon rate, 46
    discount rate, 46
    face value, 46
    government agency bonds, 48–50
    maturity, 46
    municipal bonds, 48–50
    price, 46
    quality rating, 46
    Treasury securities, 46–48
    yield, 46
budgets, 192–93. *See also* cash flow statement
Buffett, Warren, 39, 109, 229
burial arrangements, 177–78
business interests/ownerships, 56–57
business property loans, 123–24

C

California Earthquake Authority, 156
callable bonds, 46
cars
    loans and leases, 110–12
    as property, 88–89
cash
    cash compensation, 97–98
    emergency fund, 198, 207
    net worth statement, 199
cash flow statement, 191, 192–98
    expenses, 194–98
    income, 193–94
    overview, 192–93
catch-up contributions, to retirement accounts, 202
CDs (certificates of deposit), 42–43
celebration of life ceremony, 180–81
CFPB (Consumer Financial Protection Bureau), 118, 122, 128
charitable organizations, 31

checking and savings accounts, 41–42, 194
check-in gauge
    assets, 63–64, 210
    debt, 212
    estate planning, 213
    financial first aid kit, 37, 209
    financial readiness, 213
    income, 107, 211
    insurance, 167–68, 212–13
    living expenses, 212
    loans, 212
    maintaining financial readiness, 226
    purpose of, 5–6
    real estate/real property, 93, 211
    retirement planning, 78, 210
    taxes, 212
child care
    cash flow statement, 196
    living expenses, 132–33
children, information about, 24–25
Chronicle of Higher Education, The, 60
cloud storage, 6, 33
clubs and organizations, 30
    cash flow statement, 197
    living expenses, 135
C.L.U.E. report, 225
collectibles, 53–54
college savings accounts, 60–61
commercial property, 87
commercial property loans, 123–24
Common Access Card, 30
communication services, 34
community property, 172
community property with rights of survivorship, 172
consolidation of loans, 121, 128–30
Consumer Financial Protection Bureau (CFPB), 118, 122, 128
contingent beneficiary, life insurance, 159
contributions, to retirement accounts
    catch-up contributions, 202
    IRAs, 68
copyrights, 57–58, 104–5
corporate bonds, 48–50
cost basis, investments, 40
coupon rate, bonds, 46
Coverdell accounts (Education Savings Accounts), 60
credit cards, 126–28
credit reporting agencies, 221
credit report monitoring, 221–24
credit scores, 224–25
cremation, 177–78
critical emergency action list, 18
critical illness insurance, 167

current liabilities, 201
current value, assets, 198

D

DD214 (military discharge form), 30
death certificate, 231
debt, 15–16, 59–60
    business property loans, 123–24
    car loans and leases, 110–12
    on cash flow statement, 195
    check-in gauge, 139, 212
    credit cards, 126–28
    home loans, 112–19
        home equity loans, 112–14
        private mortgage insurance, 114–15
        reverse mortgages, 118–19
        time-share, 116–17
        vacation club loans, 116–17
        vacation home loans, 116
    investment property loans, 122–23
    overview, 109–10
    personal debts and loans, 125–26
    student loans, 120–22
debt consolidation loans, 121, 128–30
debt-to-income ratio, 208
defined-benefit retirement plan, 68
dental insurance, 149
Department of Defense ID Card reference center, 30
Department of Insurance (DOI), 164
dependent care spending account, 101
dependents coverage, insurance, 102
digital estate planning, 187–89
digital life, 32–35
disability insurance, 145–47
    employer/group long-term disability insurance, 145
    exclusions, 147
    future-increase option, 147
    future-purchase option, 147
    individual disability income insurance, 145
    Social Security Disability Income Insurance, 145
discount rate, bonds, 46
Disney Vacation Club, 84
Disraeli, Benjamin, 227
document retention schedule. *See* retention schedule, documents
DOI (Department of Insurance), 164
durable powers of attorney, 173

E

E&O (errors and omissions) insurance, 167
earned income, cash flow statement, 193

earnings. *See* income
education
    cash flow statement, 196
    living expenses, 132–33
Education Savings Accounts (ESAs; Coverdell accounts), 60
Eisenhower, Dwight D., 171
emergency contacts, 11
emergency fund, 198, 207
employee (group) benefits and deductions, 99–101
employee stock ownership plan (ESOP), 74
employer/group long-term disability insurance, 145
employer matching, 401(k) retirement plan, 70
Employer Retirement Accounts, 70–75
    employee stock ownership plan, 74
    401(k) plan, 70–72
    403(b) plan, 70–72
    409A plan, 74
    457 plan, 70–72
    money purchase plan, 74–75
    pension plans, 72–74
    profit-sharing plan, 75
end of life arrangements, 176–83
    appointing guardian for children, 182–83
    bequests, 183, 184
    burial and cremation, 177–78
    celebration of life ceremony, 180–81
    donation of organs/body, 176–77
    executors of, 184
    funeral and memorial services, 179–80
    letter of intent/letter of instruction, 176
    obituary, 181–83
    viewings, visitations, and wakes, 178–79
EOBs (explanation of benefits), health insurance, 153
EPO (Exclusive Provider Organization), 148
Equifax, 221, 223, 225
errors and omissions (E&O) insurance, 167
ESAs (Education Savings Accounts), 60
ESOP (employee stock ownership plan), 74
estate planning, 171–90
    Advanced Directive, 174–75
    check-in gauge, 190, 213
    digital estate planning, 187–89
    document retention schedule, 17
    ethical will, 183
    final arrangements, 176–83
        burial and cremation, 177–78
        celebration of life ceremony, 180–81
        donation of organs/body, 176–77
        funeral and memorial services, 179–80
        letter of intent/letter of instruction, 176
        obituary, 181–83
        viewings, visitations, and wakes, 178–79

Health Care Directives, 174–75
Health Care POA, 174–75
overview, 171–72
pet estate planning, 189
power of attorney, 172–74
trusts, 185–87
wills, 184–85
estimated taxes, 136–37
ethical will, 183
exchange-traded funds (ETFs), 52–53
exclusions
disability insurance, 147
property insurance, 156
Exclusive Provider Organization (EPO), 148
executors
check list for, 229–31
letter of intent/instruction for, 176
maintaining real property, 231–32
naming and authorizing, 189
paying bills, 232
paying creditors, 232
safeguarding valuable of deceased, 231
wills, 184
expense ratios, 401(k) retirement plan, 71
expenses
cash flow statement, 194–98
document retention schedule, 15–16
managing, 40
Experian, 221, 223
explanation of benefits (EOBs), health insurance, 153

F
face value, bonds, 46
FAFSA (Free Application for Financial Student Aid),
120
Fair Credit Reporting Act (FCRA), 225
Fair Isaac Corporation (FICO) score, 224–25
fair market value, assets, 198
farmland, 85–86
FCAA (Financial Counseling Association of America),
128
FCRA (Fair Credit Reporting Act), 225
FDIC (Federal Deposit Insurance Corporation), 42
Federal Emergency Management Agency (FEMA), 9
federal student loans, 120
Federal Trade Commission (FTC). See FTC
FEMA (Federal Emergency Management Agency), 9
FICO (Fair Isaac Corporation) score, 224–25
final arrangements. See end of life arrangements
financial calendar, 216–20
Financial Counseling Association of America (FCAA),
128

financial first aid kit
benefits of, 2–3
charitable organizations, 31
check-in gauge, 5–6, 37, 209
children, information about, 24–25
clubs and organizations, 30
contents of wallet, 19
critical emergency action list, 18
digital life, 32–35
emergency contacts, 11
GET READY! binder, 6
GET READY! newsletter, 7
grandchildren, information about, 25
health (medical) records, 26–27
importance of, 9
log-in credentials, 32–35
communication services, 34
financial services, 34
gaming, 34
music accounts, 34–35
shopping, 35
social media, 35
memberships, 30–31
military service, 29–30
overview, 10
personal information, 22
pet information, 27–28
retention schedule for documents, 12–17
assets, 13
debts, 15–16
estate planning, 17
expenses, 15–16
home and real estate property, 14–15
income, 15
insurance, 16–17
loans, 15–16
overview, 12
retirement plans, 14
taxes, 15–16
reward/ loyalty programs, 36
safe-deposit boxes, 20
safes, 20
Stepping In section, 7, 229–31
storage units, 20
Financial Preparedness Quiz, 3
financial ratios, 192, 207–9
debt-to-income ratio, 208
emergency fund, 207
liquidity ratio, 208
net worth ratio, 208–9
savings ratio, 208
financial readiness
cash flow statement, 192–98

check-in gauge, 213
financial ratios, 207–9
maintaining, 215–26
    check-in gauge, 226
    credit report monitoring, 221–23
    credit scores, 224–25
    financial calendar, 216–20
    identity theft, 223
    overview, 215
    specialty consumer-reporting companies, 225
net worth statement, 198–202
retirement tracker, 202–7
financial services, log-in credentials, 34
Fitch rating agency, 142
529 college savings account, 60
fixed annuities, 164
fixed-rate loans, 110
flexible spending accounts, 101
floating rate notes (FRNs), 48
401(k) retirement plan, 70–72
403(b) retirement plan, 70–72
409A retirement plan, 74
457 retirement plan, 70–72
Franklin, Benjamin, 1, 141
Free Application for Financial Student Aid (FAFSA), 120
FRNs (floating rate notes), 48
FTC (Federal Trade Commission)
    debt consolidation loans and, 128
    Guide to Credit Cards, 128
    identity theft information, 223–24
funeral services, 179–80
future-increase option, disability insurance, 147
future-purchase option, disability insurance, 147

G

gaming services, log-in credentials, 34
GET READY! binder
    parts of, 1–2
    preparing, 6
GET READY! newsletter, 7
gig (sharing) economy, 102–3
Ginnie Mae (Government National Mortgage Association [GNMA]), 50
government agency bonds, 48–50
grandchildren, including information about, 25
grants, 120
greencards, renewing/replacing, 24
group (employee) benefits and deductions, 99–101
growth stocks, 45
guardian, for children, 182–83

H

health care costs worksheets, 154–55
Health Care Directives, 174–75
Health Care POA, 174–75
health insurance, 148–55
    dental, 149
    Exclusive Provider Organization, 148
    explanation of benefits, 153
    Health Maintenance Organization, 148
    Medicare, 149–52
    Point of Service network, 148
    Preferred Provider Organization, 148
    short-term, 149
    vision, 149
Health Maintenance Organization (HMO), 148
health (medical) records, 26–27
HELOC (home equity line of credit), 112
HMO (Health Maintenance Organization), 148
home and real estate, 14–15. *See also* real estate/real property
home equity line of credit (HELOC), 112
home equity loans (second mortgages), 112–14
home inventory, 93
home loans. *See* mortgages
homeowner's insurance, 155–58
home (primary residence), 80–81

I

IBR (Income-Based Repayment) plan, 121–22
identity theft, 223–24
identity theft insurance, 167
Income-Based Repayment (IBR) plan, 121–22
income (earnings), 95–108
    basic employment earnings, 96–97
    cash compensation, 97–98
    cash flow statement, 193–94
    check-in gauge, 107, 211
    copyrights, 104–5
    dependents coverage, 102
    document retention schedule, 15
    gig economy, 102–3
    group benefits and deductions, 99–101
    investments, 106
    online income/sales, 104
    overview, 95–96
    paid time off, 98–99
    patents, 104–5
    retirement income, 107
    royalties, 104–5
    second job, 102–3
    side-hustle, 102–3
    total compensation, 102

trademarks, 104–5
indexed annuities, 164
individual disability income insurance, 145
Individual Retirement Accounts. *See* IRAs
industries, defined, 45
in-force illustrations, life insurance, 161
insurance, 141–69
    accidental death and dismemberment, 167
    annuities, 164–66
    auto, 142–45
    cash flow statement, 197–98
    check-in gauge, 167–68, 212–13
    critical illness, 167
    disability, 145–47
    document retention schedule, 16–17
    errors and omissions insurance, 167
    Federal Health Insurance Exchange, 219
    health, 148–55
        dental, 149
        Exclusive Provider Organization, 148
        explanation of benefits, 153
        Health Maintenance Organization, 148
        Medicare, 149–52
        Point of Service network, 148
        Preferred Provider Organization, 148
        short-term, 149
        vision, 149
    health care costs worksheets, 154–55
    homeowner's/renter's, 155–58
    identity theft, 167
    life, 158–61
    long-term care, 162–64
    miscellaneous, 167–68
    overview, 141–42
    personal umbrella policies, 167
    pet, 167
    travel, 167
interest rates
    applicable federal rate, 60
    fixed-rate, 110
    variable-rate, 110
intermediate bonds, 46
inter vivos (living) trusts, 186
inventory
    of home, 93
    of major property, 91–93
    of personal property, 80
    of safe/safety deposit box, 20
    of storage unit, 21
invested assets, 199–200
investment property, 84–85
investment property loans, 122–23
investments

ensuring diversified investment portfolio, 45
    income from, 106, 193
IRAs (Individual Retirement Accounts), 66–69
    contributions to, 68
    Roth IRA, 66–67
    for self-employed or small business, 68–69
    traditional IRA, 66
irrevocable trusts, 186
IRS (Internal Revenue Service)
    qualifications for being business, 103–4
    withholding calculator, 97

J

joint tenancy with rights of survivorship, 172

K

K-1 tax form, 137
KEOGH program, 68
Kimball, Spencer W., 79
Kiva loan service, 59
Knight, Bobby, 65

L

Landry, Tom, 201
leasing
    cars, 112
    residences, 130–31
legal documents. *See* personal papers and legal documents
Lending Club, 59
letter of intent/letter of instruction, 176
LexisNexis report, 225
liabilities, net worth statement, 201
life insurance, 158–61
    in-force illustrations, 161
    permanent, 159
    term, 158
line of credit, reverse mortgages, 118
liquid assets, 199
liquidity ratio, 208
living expenses, 130–35
    adult care, 132–33
    check-in gauge, 139, 212
    child care, 132–33
    clubs and organizations, 135
    education/tuition, 132–33
    memberships, 135
    rent/lease, 130–31
    season tickets, 135
    subscriptions and services, 133–34

utility/household bills, 131–32

living (inter vivos) trusts, 186

loans, 59–60. *See also* mortgages

    business property, 123–24

    car, 110–12

    cash flow statement, 195

    check-in gauge, 139, 212

    credit cards, 126–28

    debt consolidation loans, 128–30

    document retention schedule, 15–16

    fixed-rate, 110

    home loans, 112–19

    income-based repayment plans, 121

    investment property, 122–23

    personal debts and, 125–26

    secured, 110

    student, 120–22

    unsecured, 110

    variable-rate, 110

loan-to-value ratio, 116

log-in credentials, 32–35

    cloud storage, 33

    communication services, 34

    financial services, 34

    gaming, 34

    music accounts, 34–35

    password manager, 33

    shopping, 35

    social media, 35

long-term bonds, 46

long-term care insurance (LTCI), 162–64

long-term liabilities, 201

lump sum payout, reverse mortgages, 118

M

market capitalization, 45

maturity

    bonds, 46

    certificates of deposit, 43

    yield curve, 50

medical (health) records, 26–27

Medical Information Bureau (MIB) report, 225

Medicare, 149–52

memberships, 30–31

    cash flow statement, 197

    living expenses, 135

memorial services, 179–80

MIB (Medical Information Bureau) report, 225

microchips, for pets, 28

military discharge form (DD214), 30

military service, 29–30

MissingMoney.com website, 221

money market accounts, 40

money purchase plan, Employer Retirement Accounts, 74–75

monthly payout, reverse mortgages, 118

Moody's rating agency, 142

mortgages, 112–19

    home equity loans, 112–14

    private mortgage insurance, 114–15

    reverse mortgages, 118–19

    time-share, 116–17

    vacation club loans, 116–17

    vacation home, 116–17

municipal bonds (munis; muni bonds), 48–50

music accounts, log-in credentials, 34–35

mutual funds, 50–52

N

National Archives and Records Administration, 30

National Association of Estate Planners and Councils website, 171

National Association of Insurance Commissioners, 93

National Association of Unclaimed Property Administrators (NAUPA), 221

National Child Identification Program, 25

National Credit Union Insurance Fund (NCUSIF), 42

National Flood Insurance Program, 156

National Foundation for Credit Counseling (NFCC), 128

naturalization documents, 24

NAUPA (National Association of Unclaimed Property Administrators), 221

NCUSIF (National Credit Union Insurance Fund), 42

net worth ratio, 208–9

net worth statement, 191

    assets, 199–201

    liabilities, 201

    overview, 198–99

NFCC (National Foundation for Credit Counseling), 128

non-durable powers of attorney, 173

non-federal student loans, 120

non-qualified deferred compensation, 74

non-qualified stock options (NQSOs), 54

O

obituary, planning, 181–83

online income/sales, 104

open enrollment, defined, 97

organ/body donation, 176–77

ownership, property

    business interests, 56–57

community property, 172
community property with rights of survivorship, 172
defined, 40
employee stock ownership plan, 74
joint tenancy with rights of survivorship, 172
sole property, 172
tenancy by the entirety, 172
tenant-in-common, 172
time-share, 83–84
trust, 172

P

paid time off (PTO), 98–99
passports
    renewing/replacing, 24
    storing, 23
password manager, 33
patents, 57–58, 104–5
Pay As You Earn (PAYE) plan, 121
payout phase, annuities, 165
Pension Benefit Guaranty Corporation, 74
pension plans, 72–74
permanent life insurance, 159
personal debts and loans, 125–26. *See also* debt; loans
personal information, 22–23
personal papers and legal documents, 12–17
    assets, 13
    debts, 15–16
    estate planning, 17
    expenses, 15–16
    home and real estate, 14–15
    income, 15
    insurance, 16–17
    loans, 15–16
    overview, 12
    retirement plans, 14
    taxes, 15–16
personal umbrella insurance policies, 167
pet estate planning, 189
pet information, 27–28
pet insurance, 167
planes, 89–90
PMI (private mortgage insurance), 114–15
POA (Power of Attorney), 172–74
Point of Service (POS) network, 148
Power of Attorney (POA), 172–74
Preferred Provider Organization (PPO), 148
preferred stock, 44
prescriptions drug drop-off, 27
price, bonds, 46
primary residence (home), 80–81
private mortgage insurance (PMI), 114–15

profit-sharing plan, Employer Retirement Accounts, 75
property. *See also* real estate/real property
PTO (paid time off), 98–99
purging documents. *See* retention schedule, documents

Q

quality rating, bonds, 46

R

rating agencies, insurance, 142
real estate/real property, 14–15, 79–93
    boats, 89–90
    cars, 88–89
    check-in gauge, 93, 211
    commercial property, 87
    farmland, 85–86
    inventory of major property, 91–93
    investment property, 84–85
    net worth statement, 200–201
    overview, 79–80
    ownership, 40, 172
    planes, 89–90
    primary residence, 80–81
    recreational vehicles, 89–90
    time-share, 83–84
    unclaimed property, 221
    undeveloped land, 86
    vacation home, 82
recreational vehicles, 89–90
regular stock options (RSOs), 54
renter's insurance, 155–58
renting
    cars, 112
    residences, 130–31
replacement coverage, property insurance, 158
required minimum distributions (RMDs), 203
retention schedule, documents
    medical records, 27
    personal papers and legal documents, 12–17
retirement assets, net worth statement, 200
retirement income, 107, 194
retirement planning
    cash flow statement, 194
    check-in gauge, 78, 210
    document retention schedule, 14
    Employer Retirement Accounts, 70–75
        employee stock ownership plan, 74
        401(k) plan, 70–72
        403(b) plan, 70–72
        409A plan, 74
        457 plan, 70–72

money purchase plan, 74–75
    pension plans, 72–74
    profit-sharing plan, 75
  Individual Retirement Accounts, 66–69
    contributions to, 68
    Roth IRA, 66–67
    for self-employed or small business, 68–69
    traditional IRA, 66
    overview, 65–66
  social security, 76–78
retirement tracker, 192
  retirement timeline, 202–3
  savings, 204–7
reverse mortgages, 118–19
  line of credit, 118
  lump sum payout, 118
  monthly payout, 118
Revised Uniform Fiduciary Access to Digital Assets Act
    (RUFADAA), 187–88
revocable trusts, 186
reward/ loyalty programs, 36
RMDs (required minimum distributions), 203
Roth IRA, 66–67
royalties, 57–58, 104–5
RSOs (regular stock options), 54
RUFADAA (Revised Uniform Fiduciary Access to
    Digital Assets Act), 187–88
Ruff, Howard, 9

S

safe-deposit boxes, 20
safes, 20
SARSEP IRA, 68
savings
  retirement, 204–7
  savings ratio, 208
savings accounts
  college savings accounts, 60–61
  managing, 41–42
scholarships, 120
Scr.app.book app, 93
season tickets
  cash flow statement, 197
  living expenses, 135
secondary residence (vacation home), 82
secondary residence (vacation home) loans, 116
second job, income from, 102–3
second mortgages (home equity loans), 112–14
sectors, defined, 45
secured loans, 110
security freeze, credit report, 223–24
self-employed IRA, 69

separate (sole) property, 172
SEP (Simplified Employee Pension)-IRA, 68
Series EE savings bonds, 48
Series I savings bonds, 48
sharing (gig) economy, 102–3
shopping services, log-in credentials, 35
short-term bonds, 46
short-term health insurance, 149
side-hustle, 102–3
Simple IRA, 68
Simplified Employee Pension (SEP)-IRA, 68
small business IRA, 69
SOAP report, 3
social media, log-in credentials, 35
social security, 76–78
Social Security Administration (SSA), 78, 145
Social Security Disability Income Insurance (SSDI), 145
Social Security number, 223
sole (separate) property, 172
Solo 401(k) retirement plan, 68
SOs (stock options), 54–56
specialty consumer-reporting companies, 225
SSA (Social Security Administration), 78, 145
SSDI (Social Security Disability Income Insurance), 145
Standard & Poor's rating agency, 142
Stepping In section, financial first aid kit, 7, 229–31
stock options (SOs), 54–56
stocks, 44–45
  employee stock ownership plan, 74
  growth stocks, 45
  preferred stock, 44
  value stocks, 45
storage units, 20–21
student loans, 120–22
subscriptions and services, 133–34, 196–97

T

taxes, 135–39
  cash flow statement, 197
  check-in gauge, 139, 212
  document retention schedule, 15–16
  estimated taxes, 136–37
  overview, 135–37
  property, 138–39
  tax documents
    K-1, 137
    1099-B, 137
    1099-DIV, 137
    1099-G, 137
    1099-INT, 137
    1099-K, 137
    1099-MISC, 137

1099-R, 137
1099-S, 137
1099-SSA, 137
W-2G, 137
W-2 tax form, 137
tax-sheltered annuities (TSAs), 70–72
tenancy by the entirety, 172
tenant-in-common, 172
term life insurance, 158
testamentary trusts, 186
Thatcher, Margaret, 215
time-share redemption companies, 84
time-share (vacation ownership), 83–84
time-share (vacation ownership) loans, 116–17
TIPS (Treasury inflation-protected securities), 48
total compensation, 102. *See also* income (earnings)
trademarks, 57–58, 104–5
traditional IRA, 66
TransUnion, 221, 223
travel insurance, 167
Treasury bills, 47
Treasury bonds, 48
Treasury inflation-protected securities (TIPS), 48
Treasury notes, 48
Treasury securities, 46–48
    bills, 47
    bonds, 48
    floating rate notes, 48
    notes, 48
    Series EE savings bonds, 48
    Series I savings bonds, 48
    Treasury inflation-protected securities, 48
trusts, 172, 185–87
TSAs (tax-sheltered annuities), 70–72
tuition
    cash flow statement, 196
    living expenses, 132–33
Twain, Mark, 95

U

unclaimed property, searching for, 221
undeveloped land, 86
Uniformed Services ID Card, 30
Uniform Law Commission, 187

Universal Pet Microchip Lookup Tool, 28
unsecured loans, 110
utility/household bills
    cash flow statement, 195–96
    overview, 131–32

V

vacation club, 83–84
vacation club loans, 116–17
vacation home (secondary residence), 82
vacation home (secondary residence) loans, 116
vacation ownership (time-share), 83–84
vacation ownership (time-share) loans, 116–17
vaccination records, pets, 28
value stocks, 45
variable annuities, 164
variable-rate loans, 110
vision insurance, 149

W

W-2G tax form, 137
W-2 tax form, 137
wakes, 178–79
wallet, listing contents of in financial first aid kit, 19
wills, 184–85
withdrawals
    from annuities, 164
    from certificates of deposit, 42
    from retirement accounts, 65, 68, 107, 203
withholding calculator (IRS), 97
Wooden, John, 2
The Work Number report, 225

Y

yield, bonds
    corporate bonds, 50
    defined, 46
    government agency bonds, 50
    municipal bonds, 50
    yield curve, 50

About the Author

When life decides it's time for a crisis, it's likely most of us are unprepared. My greatest passion is to help you GET READY! for those life changing events by showing you how to create and maintain a financial first aid kit and become financially prepared.

I'm a teacher with a sense of humor.

I love helping others makes sense of the financial world in way that is easy to understand. I get that we all don't speak insurance-ese or financial-ese. As a financial guy with a knack for writing, my goal is to guide you through the insurance and financial worlds using language and laughs that everyone can understand. As a result, my first book, *Questions and Answers on Life Insurance*, was born in 2004 and opened up a new path for financial literacy.

Since then, book writing has led to many media interviews, guest articles, and the launch of the GET READY! Initiative, which includes the GET READY! with Tony Steuer Podcast, GET READY! Financial Preparedness Clubs, and the GET READY! Financial Standards designed to protect your financial interests.

I love learning.

The world of finances and insurance is always changing (e.g., new president = new health care). Stick with me, and I'll keep you on top of the financial and insurance worlds. Being financially and insurance organized was a must when my young son was diagnosed with Type 1 diabetes a few years ago. I learned how to access resources for my son.

When I'm not helping others GET READY!, you might find me cheering on the Warriors with the latest IPA, playing basketball with my friends, enjoying some Grateful Dead tunes, or reading a great mystery or history book. My greatest joy is being Cheryl's husband and Avery's dad.

My goal is to always treat you with respect and to help guide you to make the best insurance-related decisions for your needs. Running a business with integrity is important to me.

So, let's stay connected. Visit tonysteuer.com to assess your financial preparedness, sign up for the GET READY! Newsletter, download checklists, and join the community discussion.

Looking forward to helping you GET READY!

Tony

THE OFFICIAL BIO

Tony Steuer has led the way in establishing a path for financial preparedness through his award winning books:

*Insurance Made Easy**

*Questions and Answers on Life Insurance: The Life Insurance Toolbook*** ***

*The Questions and Answers on Life Insurance Workbook**

The Questions and Answers on Disability Insurance Workbook

The Questions and Answers on Insurance Planner

*Awarded the Apex Award for Publication

**Awarded the Excellence in Financial Literacy Education (EIFLE) Award from the Institute of Financial Literacy

***Named as one of the top Nine Great Investment Books Worth Reading by *Forbes*

Tony regularly consults with InsureTechs, financial planners, insurance agencies, attorneys, insurance companies, and other financial service companies on insurance marketing and product best practices and on strategies to help consumers GET READY! through financial preparedness and the Financial Integrity Pledge. Tony is a past member of the California Department of Insurance Curriculum Board and current member of the National Financial Educator's Council (NFEC) Curriculum Advisory Board.

He is regularly featured in the media. Tony has appeared in interviews for the *New York Times*, the *Washington Post, U.S. News & World Report*, Slate.com, BottomLine Personal, BankRate.com, Insure .com, InsuranceQuotes.com, Mint.com, You and Your Family, and BenefitsPro.com. He has appeared as a guest on the *Wall Street Journal Morning Radio Show, Prudent Money Show, Your Financial Editor, Insider Secrets, Suzy G. in the Morning Show, Financial Finesse*, GrowingMoney.com, Nolo.com, TheNest .com, LovetoKnow.com, and LifeInsuranceSelling.com. Tony also served as a technical editor for *The Retirement Bible* and *The Investing Bible*.

He is passionate about giving back. Tony is involved with many worthwhile causes, including Diabetes Youth Families (board member), Alameda Community Learning Center (board member), Creative Community Education Foundation (Treasurer), and St. Joseph's Elementary School (former school advisory board member), and he is a member of the Lucille Packard Children's Hospital Foundation Advisory Council. Tony has also been a coach for his son's Catholic Youth Organization Basketball team and Little League Baseball team, taught wilderness first aid and white-water rescue, volunteered as a white-water raft guide, and performed improvisational comedy.

Tony Steuer lives in Alameda, California.

Made in the USA
Middletown, DE
04 January 2022

57733365R00144